When he died in 1919, the Lancet medical journal described him as "the greatest personality in the medical world at this time." Thirty years later, I came to Oxford as a medical student. The reputation of Osler then, as a former Regius Professor of Medicine, was unparalleled. We saw him as the man who had brought science into medical education on both sides of the Atlantic. Moreover he was also seen to have demonstrated that compassionate medical care and science were not only compatible but both necessary – and that careful clinical observation was essential to diagnosis. "If you listen to the patient he will tell you the diagnosis." It is clear that Osler commanded enormous admiration and respect amongst colleagues, students and patients. David Cranston's splendid succinct account of his life and work is warmly welcomed. It admirably reflects the personality of this remarkable man.

*Godfrey Fowler OBE FRCP FRCGP, Emeritus Professor*
*of General Practice, University of Oxford*

It has been a pleasure to read David Cranston's admirably concise story of William Osler's life and career. Having worked where he first practiced, seen the pathological specimens he prepared and felt his ghost walking the corridors of McGill's medical school, we delighted in finding the same ghost in Oxford. We first lived on Bradmore Road, within view of 13 Norham Gardens, home of Sir William. We could sense his spirit which pervades this history. His view of professionals is that: "The practice of medicine is an art, not a trade; a calling, not a business; a calling in which your heart will be exercised equally with your head." These critical ideas come through very clearly in David Cranston's text. It was a delightful read.

*Jonathan L. Meakins OC, MD, DSc, FRCS(Hon.), FRCS(C., Glas.),*
*FACS, Emeritus Professor of Surgery, University of Oxford. Formally*
*Archibald Professor and Chair of Surgery, McGill University.*

William Osler was one of the founding fathers of the Johns Hopkins Hospital. It was there that he wrote his famous textbook *The Principles and Practice of Medicine* and revolutionised the teaching of medicine taking students to the bedside. David Cranston's biography will help to keep his name alive, and in these days of increasing technological advance remind all those involved in health care that humanity must remain central, and that, in Osler's own words "the patient who has the disease is more important than the disease that has the patient".

*Professor Robert Montgomery MD, DPhil, FACS*
*Director of the New York University Langone Transplant Institute.*
*Formerly Director of the Comprehensive Transplant Center The Johns*
*Hopkins Hospital*

# William Osler
## and his
# Legacy to Medicine

# William Osler
# and his
# Legacy to Medicine

*Paul + Joan*

*with love*

*Dave*

*27 Sept 2017*

## David Cranston
Illustrated by Valerie Petts

*Sir William Osler*

**David Cranston** completed his medical training in Bristol and worked in Exeter and Bath before coming to Oxford for post-graduate doctoral research. He is a Fellow of the Royal College of Surgeons of England and is currently Consultant Urological Surgeon in the Oxford University Hospitals NHS Trust, Associate Professor of Surgery in the Nuffield Department of Surgical Science and a Fellow of Green Templeton College, Oxford and joint curator of 13 Norham Gardens. Outside medicine he serves as a licensed lay minister in the Church of England and is on the board of the Oxford Centre for Mission Studies.

**Valerie Petts** first started training as a lab technician in Professor Howard Florey's department in Oxford before working in clinical immunology research in London and Sydney and has now been painting full-time since about 1990. She has had numerous exhibitions in England and has also exhibited in Tokyo and Cape Town. She has illustrated five books including Oxford Words and Watercolours, Consider England, John Radcliffe and his Legacy to Oxford, Penicillin and the Legacy of Norman Heatley, and a visitors' book for the National Trust.

# FOREWORD

More than any other single figure, William Osler defined the framework for medicine in the 20th century. His remarkable insights and influence established an approach to bedside medicine that brought the field firmly into the scientific arena for the first time. This excellent book by David Cranston recounts Osler's journey from the town of his birth in Ontario, though academic appointments at McGill, University of Pennsylvania, Johns Hopkins and, ultimately, Oxford. For all physicians, the history of his life and accomplishments reminds us of how much progress was made by applying relatively few scientific tools in the context of acute bedside observation and careful history taking. The problem that Osler addressed throughout his career was one of disease definition and he, more than any physician of his era, was able to use combination of anatomic pathology, microbiology and clinical bedside skills to create a new framework for defining disease. In his textbook, The Principles and Practice of Medicine, he lays out with acuity the classification of disease, much of which holds true today. His clinical skills, particularly his ability to transmit his remarkable understanding of disease to others has placed him in a class of his own on both sides of the Atlantic.

His influence still can be felt in Oxford medicine today. The tools available for defining disease are now much more refined and precise, but the recognition that by understanding the underpinning mechanisms of disease one can ultimately provide a greatly improved approach to therapy coupled to a more accurate understanding of natural history. In many ways, medicine has entered a whole new era of precision medicine, but the fundamental principles of applying scientific method for refining disease definition can be tracked to Osler.

Osler's story describes a man who attained much academically and professionally, but also describes a man with his own human, and sometimes tragic, elements. This book reinforces the need to understand this individual if one is to understand medicine as we know it today.

Professor Sir John Bell, GBE FRS,
Regius Professor of Medicine, Oxford

# ACKNOWLEDGEMENTS

I am grateful to Professor Sir John Bell for his foreword. He follows Osler as the second Canadian to become Regius Professor of Medicine in Oxford. Professor Jonathan Meakins was the former Archibald Professor and Chair of Surgery at McGill University, and Professor Robert Montgomery was the former Chief of the Division of Transplantation and Director of the Comprehensive Transplant Centre at Johns Hopkins. I am grateful to them for their commendations along with that of Professor Godfrey Fowler Emeritus Professor of General Practice at Oxford University.

Mrs Mary Weston, Professor Max Blythe and Dr Chris Winearls have been very helpful in proof reading the text and making helpful comments. Valerie Petts has enhanced this book tremendously by her beautiful watercolours, while Tony Gray has been very helpful and patient as both editor and publisher through his company WORDS BY DESIGN. Lastly but by no means least to my wife Rosie for her support over 40 years of marriage.

# Dedication

In memory of
Dr Montagu Gordon Barker ('Monty') FRCPE, FRCPsych
1934-2015
Mentor and Friend

and for his wife Rosemary who like Grace Osler
married a man who had books all over the floor,
where the dining room table was always covered,
and whose house was never cleared.

# CONTENTS

# INTRODUCTION

Patients are people too, and one day all doctors will become patients. Woe betide the doctor who lets humanity slip out of medicine. In the current practice of medicine it is all too easy to looks at computers, charts and scans and ignore the patient. Osler never forgot the patient and we would do well to learn from him. He had many quotes which are seen in the pages of this book, but one of the most important is that "it is more important to know about the patient who has the disease than the disease that has the patient". His quotes may appear sexist referring just to the men, but in his day there were few female medical students and no doubt today he would have treated all equally as he did with everyone else with whom he came into contact.

As a medical student I thought that urological surgery was a cinderella specialty, but when I became a consultant I found that many of my colleagues were asking me to see their fathers, sometimes their mothers, and twenty year later, asking me to see themselves. Many of the patients who have been through our department in Oxford over the years, are interesting people with a lifetime's history behind them. If Osler were alive today he would soon have pointed out, had I taken an incomplete clinical history and ignored the social side, that I would have missed men and women who fought at sea in the Battle of Jutland in 1916, or on land in the Mud of Ypres where Osler's son, Revere, died in 1917. Others served at sea in the Arctic Convoys or in the air in as fighter pilots or bomber crews in the Second World War. One served abroad the Royal Yacht, another acted as the Queen's chauffeur, one was in Dublin at the Easter rising of 1916 and another in Moscow in 1917 during the Russian revolution.

I often ask students what is the most important question to ask a man in his nineties who comes to my clinic. It is not about his symptoms and it is nothing to do with urology but what they did in the Second World War. In ten years these people will be no more and now is the chance to experience living history. A hundred years ago Osler met men who had fought in the Crimea and his mother was alive at the Battle of Waterloo in 1815 and walked from Hampstead to Bushy Park at age of nine to bring news of the victory.

As doctors we are not only clinicians and  teachers, but we are also role models for those around us. When we teach at the bedside or in clinic  we are watched and observed as to how we treat our patients and our staff. It give insight into our values in life, our goals and beliefs.

Osler was famous for many things including his quotes, many of which are found at the bottom of the pages of this book, but perhaps Osler had no greater accolade than his reputation among the clinical students who said that, "If you wanted to see the chief at his best, watch him as he passes the bedside of some poor old soul with a chronic and hopeless malady as they always get his best".

Would that was true of all of us who are in the so called 'caring professions' today. One day we too will be in the bed rather than standing at the foot of it.

# CHAPTER 1: BEGINNINGS

On 12th July 1849 a seventh child was born to missionary parents in the backwoods of Ontario. His destiny would be to revolutionise the medical education system across the globe.

This child born to Featherstone Lake Osler and his wife Ellen in Bond Head, Ontario, was named after William of Orange, the victor at the Battle of the Boyne in 1690, for 12th July is the day on which the battle is commemorated. He was born at home, attended by the local doctor, a graduate of Trinity College Dublin, who, as he would remind students many years later, "Came many weary miles across the backwoods of Canada to usher me into this breathing world."

William Osler's forebears were a Cornish seafaring family. His great-grandfather, Edward Osler, was a merchant seaman who died in the West Indies following a wound. His grandfather was a ship owner at Falmouth, and a former Lieutenant in the Royal Navy who served on the HMS Victory, although not at the Battle of Trafalgar.

When a teenager, William's father, Featherstone Osler, served on *HMS Sappho* when it was nearly destroyed by Atlantic storms and left adrift for weeks. He survived, and in 1832 was invited to serve on *HMS Beagle* as the scientific officer on Charles Darwin's historic voyage to the Galapagos Islands, an invitation he had to turn down as his own father was dying.

Soon after, his father changed vocation, entered St Catharine's Hall Cambridge to train for the ministry, and was

*Birthplace of William Osler*

ordained by the Archbishop of Canterbury in Lambeth Palace in 1837. He emigrated to Canada and became a 'saddle-bag minister' with his young wife Ellen Pickton, who was described as, "a very pretty girl, clever, witty, lively and good-tempered, and very faithful in her friendships." They found their way to Bond Head in the Canadian wilderness where the early Christian settlers needed ministers of the Gospel to care for their spiritual needs. The nearest post office was twelve miles away and the nearest doctor fifteen.

Life in the Canadian wilderness was hard, and Ellen described how her husband was away from Tuesday to Friday every week riding over swamps and trails, often crossing bridges made of floating logs fastened together with rope. A younger sister to William was born but died at the age of three. For the surviving eight children, outdoor activities in

*A physician who treats himself has a fool for a patient.*

the Canadian backwoods included skating and snowboarding in winter, fishing and swimming in summer, playing by the sawmill at the foot of the hill and romping with Rover the Newfoundland dog, who was trained to go alone to Bond Head for the mail.

As the family grew, it was decided to move to a larger community to benefit the education of the children. In 1857, when the rectorship of Ancaster and Dundas became vacant, Featherstone Osler was granted the living and the family took up residence in Dundas, which was to be their home for the next 25 years.

William Osler always had a vivid recollection of his boyhood in Canada, and the happy spring days when:

*We went off to the bush to make maple syrup on the bright sunny days, with delicious cold nights, campfires, log cabins and the fascinating work of tapping the trees. Putting in the birch bark sprouts, arranging the troughs and then going from tree to tree collecting the clear sap which we boiled down to make the maple syrup.*

*There are incurable diseases in medicine, incorrigible vices in the ministry; insoluble cases in law.*

# CHAPTER 2: SCHOOL

William progressed well at Barrie Grammar School where he was top of his year and notably proficient in "that greatest of all books, the Bible." In 1866 he went to Trinity College School in Weston near Toronto, where he was an active and mischievous child, and known for practical jokes. On one occasion at school it landed his group in prison for a couple of days when they barricaded a housekeeper into her room for spilling slops on the stairs and soaking one of the boys. Having trapped her in her room they had made a paste of molasses, mustard and pepper, which they put on the stove so that the fumes rose through the air into the room where the housekeeper was a prisoner. The matron did not share the joke and was not prepared for the boys just to receive a beating, which they duly did with hickory canes. Instead she insisted on an arrest warrant for them. This was impossible to achieve in Weston and so she applied for it in Toronto, where eventually William's elder brother, a lawyer, defended them, and having paid the appropriate fine they were released.

William Osler initially planned to follow his father into the ministry. The warden of Trinity College School was the Reverend William Johnson who was not only an Anglican priest and schoolmaster but also a keen biologist. He introduced Osler to microscopy, and showed him how to mount slides. Even at this young age William took the *Microscopical Journal* and began to document his discoveries in a notebook, a habit that he was to keep for the rest of his

*Osler as a youth at Trinity College*

life. His love of books was encouraged, first from his father's theological library and second from the classics in the Weston school library.

Following a rugby injury at school he developed osteomyelitis in one of his legs and was confined to bed for several weeks. It was during this time that he had long talks with the Warden, who encouraged him in his experimental activities. At school Johnson also used to read aloud to the boys selected extracts from *Religio Medici*, a book written by Sir Thomas Browne, who had lived through the greater part of the seventeenth century. Browne wrote with wit and humour on a wide range of subjects including science, medicine and religion. This book became Osler's favourite, and lay on his coffin 52 years later.

William was a fine all-round athlete, a keen cricketer and an excellent bowler. On one occasion he broke the school record for throwing the cricket ball, throwing it so far that it hit the top of a boundary fence. Professor Jones, a mathematician from Trinity College Toronto, estimated that if the fence had not been in the way it would have beaten the best throw at Eton or Rugby. However, the English schools never yielded their claim on the strength of Professor Jones' verdict.

Another influence on Osler's life was James Bovell. He was a medical director at Trinity College in Toronto and used to spend time at Trinity College School, Weston, where he first encountered William, then head prefect. It was the inspiration of Johnson and Bovell that persuaded him to turn to medicine,

*Who serves the gods dies young.*
*Venus Bacchus and Vulcan send no bills in the seventh decade.*

although when he went up to Trinity College in Toronto in the autumn of 1867 he was still considering reading theology. He had won the Dixon Prize Scholarship, and Trinity was regarded as a nursery for students of divinity, while science was thought of as a hobby rather than a proper subject for study. However, after returning to Trinity College in 1868 for the second year he announced to his parents and to the Provost his determination to enter medicine, and having done so it was not long before his first article appeared in print entitled, 'Christmas and the Microscope'.

*Commonsense nerve fibres are seldom medullated before 40 they are never seen even with the microscope before 20.*

# CHAPTER 3: MCGILL

At Trinity College, Osler was known to spend more time in the dissecting room than any of the students. He frequently brought in his lunch and continued all day. On one occasion he pointed out the presence of the *Trichina spiralis* in one of the muscles which nobody else had observed. *Trichina spiralis* is a parasite occurring in various animals and humans, responsible for the disease trichinosis. It is sometimes referred to as the 'pork worm' as it is often found in undercooked pork.

Osler became very interested in the study of parasites and began visiting the veterinary hospital, drawn there by his interest in comparative parasitology and the expectation of adding to his growing collection of various parasites, known as enterozoa, that live in the internal organs of animals.

## McGill

In 1870 he switched universities to complete his medical studies in the more prestigious McGill University Faculty of Medicine, where he described the two valuable assets for the students: "Much acute disease and a group of keen teachers."

Bovell had emigrated to the West Indies, so Osler had lost one friend, but in Montreal he found another in Robert Palmer Howard, Dean and Professor of Medicine at McGill. Osler said that he owed his success in life to Johnson, Bovell and Howard. It was while at McGill that he discovered the writings of Thomas Carlyle, and throughout his life often quoted Carlyle's admonition to,

*Osler as a student at McGill, 1871*

*Ignore what lies dimly at a distance; do what lies clearly at hand.*

Despite his hospital clerking duties he found time for reading and enlarging his collection of entozoa. Specimens were obtained from many sources including the numerous rats that had made their home in the hospital.

He read widely, and it was at this early period that he began his lifelong habit of reading for half-an-hour in bed every night before putting out the light, a discipline he would encourage in his students for the rest of his life. The books he recommended as a student's bedside library were those with which he was familiar in his early days, especially his favourite *Religio Medici* by Thomas Browne.

He also came under the influence of George Campbell, Dean and Professor of Surgery, who was trained in the days before anti-sepsis was understood. Lister, who was responsible for initiating anti-sepsis, was only just coming into prominence as the new Professor of Surgery in Edinburgh. The surgeon of the day operated in his ordinary clothes, collar and cuffs, possibly with a frockcoat if he was more particular,

*Although one swallow does not make a summer, one tophus makes gout and one crescent malaria.*

and this would have been the surgical environment with which the young William would have been familiar. In 1872 Osler qualified, coming first in the final examination, receiving his medical degree, *Medicinae Doctor et Chirurgiae Magister* (Doctor of Medicine and Master of Surgery) and was allowed to put the initials MDCM after his name.

*The young doctor should look about early for a pastime, that will take him away from patients, pills, and potions.*

# CHAPTER 4: EUROPE

After graduating Osler was thinking of a career in ophthalmology, but first he arranged a trip to Europe, then the centre of the medical world, thanks to a generous gift of $1,000 from his brother Edmund. He sailed to Ireland where he visited the Giant's Causeway, and then on to London where he spent some time at University College Hospital working with a physiologist, John Burdon Sanderson, who had become Medical Officer for Health for Paddington in 1856. Sanderson was studying infectious disease and had recently noted that some moulds, probably *Penicillium*, inhibited certain bacteria. Sadly he did not pursue this further. Osler spent several fruitful months in Sanderson's laboratory, where he made some observations on platelets which remained one of his most original scientific achievements. Thirty-four years later Osler would succeed Sanderson as the Regius Professor of Medicine at Oxford.

He travelled to Berlin where Virchow, the founder of modern pathology, and Langenbeck, were still working. Langenbeck was a bold and skilful surgeon, whose retractor is still in common use today. He described Langenbeck's clinic, where students were allowed to smoke.

*Often by the time the patient was brought in the condition of the atmosphere was such that you had to look across the large theatre from the top and the men on the opposite side were seen through a blue haze. Quite a number of the students were badly marked with sword cuts received in duels.*

On Monday mornings he watched Virchow, who performed post-mortems with such care and minuteness that three or four hours might elapse before they were finished. The very first morning of his attendance, Virchow spent as long as half-an-hour in the description of the skull cap. On Wednesdays and Saturdays other demonstrations took place in a large lecture theatre accommodating 140 students, with the table so arranged that the microscopes on which specimens were mounted circulated around continuously on small tramways.

Osler was in Europe on 24th December 1873 when a prosperous Baltimore merchant, Johns Hopkins, died leaving his fortune 'to foster higher education'. Osler was unaware of this at the time and the effect it was to have on his future career. After leaving Berlin he arrived in Vienna on 1st January 1874 with a new notebook in his pocket. He was not impressed with the pathology there!

*Having watched Virchow conduct post-mortems in Berlin it was painful to attend the ones in Vienna as they were performed in such a slovenly manner.*

He visited the surgeon Billroth and decided to take a course of operations from his assistant before he left. Billroth, who is regarded as the founder of modern abdominal surgery, gave his name to operations on the stomach. He was also a talented musician, a close friend of Brahms, and a leading patron of the Viennese musical scene.

*No human being is constituted to know the truth, the whole truth and nothing but the truth; and even the best of men must be content with fragments, with partial glimpses, never the full fruition.*

14

In April, Osler returned to London to complete the paper on his research in Sanderson's laboratory, and during his time there he met Charles Darwin at an evening soirée who he described as, "An old man with bushy eyebrows who spoke pleasantly of the Principal of McGill College." It is not clear if they discussed his father's invitation to travel on Darwin's voyage in 1832 on *HMS Beagle*.

*The philosophies of one age have become the absurdities of the next, and the foolishness of yesterday has become the wisdom of tomorrow.*

# CHAPTER 5: RETURN TO MCGILL

He returned to Canada in 1874 with empty pockets. He was anxiously looking for a job, and was able to take over the work of the local doctor in Dundas. His first fee as a practising physician, which he entered into his account book, read, 'Speck in cornea... 50c'.

In July he received a letter from McGill University offering him a job as lecturer which he duly accepted. It was not long before he started the first Journal Club encouraging discussion of recent papers describing the latest developments in medicine. As far as his lectures went, it appears that the content was often better than the delivery. The following year he gave the valedictory address to the graduating class of students where his speech reflected the type of address that he would give for the rest of his life. He pointed out that their training was incomplete, that they must always be students, that they should keep up with their reading, and get into the habit of attending societies and reporting their experience. He went on to say that their behaviour was more likely to bring them success than a stream of diplomas.

At this time smallpox was rife in seaport towns. Vaccination was not compulsory, and attached to the hospital was an isolated smallpox ward in which it was the custom for members of the attending staff to serve successively for a period of three months. Although he was not officially on the hospital staff, Osler volunteered to serve on the smallpox ward. During his time there he contracted smallpox, although

*Medical Building, McGill, courtesy of Professor Jonathan Meakins*[1]

fortunately in a mild form from which he recovered completely.

During that time he looked after a young Englishman who was in Montreal on business and developed smallpox from which he subsequently died. Osler wrote a very caring letter to the boy's parents in England. Some 30 years later, when he was Regius Professor in Oxford, he met a lady at dinner who, intrigued by his name, said that a young brother had gone out to Montreal and been cared for during a fatal illness by a doctor called Osler who had sent a sympathetic letter to the boy's parents. She added that her mother was still living in

*The greater the ignorance the greater the dogmatism.*

the south of England and hoped that she might meet the man who had written the letter. Thus it was that on a trip to Cornwall Osler paid a visit to their bereaved mother, taking with him a photograph of the boy's grave which he had sent to Montreal to obtain.

In 1876 he was appointed pathologist to the Montreal General Hospital, having given up the idea of specialising in ophthalmology, and in 1878 he was unexpectedly appointed senior physician ahead of the assistant physicians, one of whom was expecting to be appointed. Osler's experience in the post-mortem room and his clinical work during the smallpox epidemic swung the governors in favour of his appointment. Before taking up this post he made a further trip to London where he passed the examination for Membership of the Royal College of Physicians, adding MRCP to his name.

In 1880 Koch gave a celebrated address in which, for the first time, he provided the evidence that tuberculosis was a highly infectious bacterial disease affecting both man and animals. In July that year Osler demonstrated the presence of the organism in the lung of a man who had died from tuberculosis.

The following year he was back in London to attend a medical conference under the presidency of Sir James Paget. Paget was a famous surgeon and pathologist who gave his name to Paget's disease, a chronic disorder leading to misshapen bones.

*Osler in 1881*

*There are only two sorts of doctors:*
*those who practice with their brains,*
*and those who practice with their tongues.*

The conference drew 3,000 doctors from all parts of the world and was attended by the Prince of Wales and the Crown Prince of Prussia. Virchow was present and spoke on the value of pathological experiments and Pasteur described his recent experiments showing that animals could be protected against certain diseases by vaccination.

*The old Pathological Museum of McGill University (burnt down in 1907), as it was when William Osler worked on his collection in 1905. Many of the specimens on the shelves were placed there by Osler himself in 1877-84.*

*The good physician treats the disease;*
*the great physician treats the patient who has the disease.*

# CHAPTER 6: PENNSYLVANIA

Over the following three years Osler consolidated his work in Montreal, but in June 1884 he received a letter inviting him to the chair of Clinical Medicine at the University of Pennsylvania in Philadelphia. The University had been about to appoint an internal candidate, but they were encouraged to look further afield, after one senior faculty member wrote:

*I have no doubt that Osler is the best man. He has every social need, is aged 35 and has won distinction as an investigator and writer, as well as being a competent teacher, and will therefore add to our illustriousness.*

He accepted the invitation and was duly appointed. It was a sideways step and an unusual move for North America at the time, although common enough in Europe. It caused a great deal of comment, although more was positive than negative.

He left a considerably legacy of his brief period at McGill, where he had introduced modern methods of teaching physiology, and edited the first clinical and pathological reports issued by the Montreal General Hospital – the first by any Canadian hospital. He had written many papers, performed almost 1,000 autopsies, made numerous preparations of important specimens for museums, and encouraged the development of closer relations with Montreal Veterinary College. On the national scene he occupied senior roles in the Canadian Medical Association as Secretary in 1881 and President in 1884. He had shown courage in attending the smallpox wards, and on the personal front always had a reputation for being hard-working, showing charity in his dealings with his fellow physicians and generosity to his students. He was cheery and kind to all, whether rich or poor, young or old, learned or ignorant, and he never seemed to get upset with people who came to him for advice or interrupted what he was doing at the time.

These qualities earned him great popularity, which he retained throughout his life. He frequently referred to himself as a notebook man, for he always read with pen and paper in hand and would jot down any useful quotation which he might want to use later, or a thought which had come to mind in relation to something on which he was working. If a notebook was not at hand he would write on fragments of paper or on the blank flyleaves of a book he happened to be reading at the time.

Arriving in Philadelphia on 11th October 1884, the first impression of the students was one of disappointment. He seemed to be informal and unpolished. Instead of descending from a carriage, he jumped down from the streetcar carrying a small black satchel containing his lunch, with a bundle of books and papers under his arm. He wore a frock coat, top hat, flowing red necktie, low shoes, heavy socks, and sported a drooping moustache, entering by the side door rather than the main entrance.

Although Osler did not have the eloquence of his predecessor, when the students came in contact with him on the wards and at the bedside – a novelty in the Philadelphia school – the situation was entirely different. There he had an

*The first duties of the physician is to educate*
*the masses not to take medicine.*

increasingly enthusiastic group about him and his teaching produced such an atmosphere that the young students described him as, "A breath of fresh air let into a stifling room." Disappointment gave way to devotion. His bedside teaching was inspiring, and his weekly lectures were always illustrated by pathological examples of the disease about which he was speaking.

He made many friends in Philadelphia among the medical fraternity, including Samuel Gross and his wife, Grace. Samuel's father, who had died the previous year, was one of the outstanding figures in American surgery. He was noted for his hospitality, a tradition which his son carried on, and Samuel's wife came to regard this as part of her calling. So it was natural enough that they should have called on Osler in his rooms shortly after his arrival. Here they found a homesick man, pestered by mosquitoes, sweltering in the heat of a breathless October evening, and delighted to be invited to Sunday dinner the following day. It was the start of a great friendship.

If he was not being entertained on Sunday he would often be seen in the post-mortem room, and if he found something particularly interesting he would send a runner out to gather the students and show them what he had found. He was not afraid to admit his mistakes, and on one occasion at the bedside he demonstrated a gentleman with pneumonia. The man subsequently died, and at post-mortem Osler found no pneumonia, but a pleural effusion. He sent for all those in his class, showing them the mistake he had made, discussed how it might have been avoided, and encouraged them not to make the same error.

While Osler had a huge capacity for work he was also able to relax and particularly enjoyed being with children. One of

*The desire to take medicine is perhaps the greatest feature which distinguishes man from animals.*

the places where he was best known in Philadelphia was at the toy counter in one of the big stores, and the sales girls used to draw lots to see who could wait on him. He always bought something, made up his mind quickly, gave an address to which the purchase was to be sent, and left behind him the small coins given in change.

He became one of the seven founding members of the Association of American Physicians. The inaugural meeting was held in 1886 in Washington, and in an article 30 years later he spoke of this meeting as the coming-of-age party of internal medicine in America. He presented a classic paper to this first meeting on a rare condition of the valves of the heart ('On the Nature and Complications of the Biscuspid Aortic Heart Valve').

Later that summer he took a five-week holiday in British Columbia, the first break he had had for many years. Much of it was spent in bark canoes with Native American Indians as guides. Many years afterwards he drew analogies from his observations:

> There are two great types of practitioners, the routinist and the rationalist.... The mind, like the body, falls only too readily into the rut of oft-repeated experiences. One evening in the far north-west beneath the shadow of the Rocky Mountains we camped beside a small lake from which, diverging in all directions, were deep furrows, each one as straight as an arrow as far as the eye could reach. They were the deep ruts of tracks which countless generations of buffalo had worn in the prairie as they followed each other to and from the water. In our minds, countless, oft-repeated experiences wear similar ruts in

*The best preparation for tomorrow is to do today's work superbly well.*

*which we find it easiest to travel, and out of which many*
*of us never dream of straying.*

Back in Philadelphia he spent some of his time researching malaria, and wrote a general summary on it which was published in the *British Medical Journal* in 1887. Even before the full life-cycle of the malarial parasite was known, he suggested that,

> *In malarial regions the examination of the blood will prove, in skilled hands, a most valuable aid in the diagnosis of many obscure cases.*

As Professor of Medicine he was intimately involved in student examinations and, while he was generally very supportive of the students, his clinical assistant recalls telling him one day that the boys were very much afraid of the approaching examination, to which he replied: "I mean them to be. I am examining in the interests of the public, not of the students."

However, he also felt that it was the examiner's duty to dwell upon the student's character and his method of attacking the problem at hand rather than on the number of facts he could retain in his mind, and in this he often ran counter to the prevailing custom.

He was not a great one for modern contraptions, and was certainly not in favour of telephones when they were beginning to be put into doctors' offices. He found them distracting rather than useful, although he did have the ability from an early age to switch off when other things were going on around him. His memory for names throughout his life

*Live neither in the past nor in the future, but let each day's work*
*absorb your entire energies, and satisfy your widest ambition.*

was described as uncanny and he seldom forgot a student's name. This may be ascribed to his early training at Weston school where as head prefect it was necessary, on the unexpected order from the headmaster, to call the role of the school from memory to see if any boy was playing truant.

Known as 'a doctor's doctor', he was not always able to cure his patients, but was invariably a source of strength and comfort to them. When William Keen, a senior surgeon at Philadelphia, called urgently one day after his wife was taken ill at their cottage on Cape Cod, Osler came, but neither he nor another surgical colleague were able to do anything to help. Nevertheless Osler stayed. Thirty years later he received a letter from Keen in which he said

> *You sat with me long into the night listening while I bared my very soul to you. What a comfort you were to me you cannot guess.*

It was in 1888, at the third conference of the American Medical Association, that the President, John Billings, was often seen in Osler's company. Billings was also the medical advisor of the Johns Hopkins trustees, and the close association of the two led to rumours that this institution was courting Osler. Osler's recollection of the meeting was that Billings asked him if he would take charge of the medical department of the new Johns Hopkins Hospital, and without a moment's hesitation Osler answered, "Yes." According to Osler, the meeting was over in a couple of minutes.

While Osler's recollection of the matter may not have been entirely correct, the minutes on 25th September 1888 of the Johns Hopkins trustees recorded that they agreed to appoint

*The value of experience is not in seeing much, but in seeing wisely.*

Osler as Physician-in-Chief to the hospital. It was only four years since he had arrived in Philadelphia.

Later Osler was to write:

*The opening of the Johns Hopkins Hospital in 1889 marked a new style in medical education in the United States. It was not the hospital in itself, as there were many larger and just as good. It was not the men appointed, as there were others just as well qualified. It was the organisation. For the first time in an English-speaking country the hospital was organised in units, each one under the direction of a head or chief.*

In 1889 Osler was to suffer two body blows that affected him deeply. Late in March came word that Howard Palmer, his friend and mentor in Montreal, had been taken ill, so Osler left for Montreal to see him, and was with him until his death at the end of March. However, even before his return to Philadelphia news came of the sudden illness of Samuel Gross who he found critically ill on his return, suffering from a virulent bout of pneumonia. On 16th April Gross died at his home where Osler had spent many happy hours.

On the morning of 1st May 1889 he gave his now famous valedictory address to the Pennsylvania students entitled 'Aequanimitas', on the subject of imperturbability and equanimity necessary for the practice of medicine, and then left for Baltimore.

*The very first step towards success in any occupation is to become interested in it.*

# Chapter 7: Johns Hopkins

Johns Hopkins was a Baltimore merchant who, with his brothers, established Hopkins & Brothers Wholesalers in 1819. However, the majority of his fortune was made by his investments in different ventures, most notably the Baltimore and Ohio Railway Company. A bachelor and a Quaker with a simple lifestyle, he believed that there were two things that would always last – a university, for there will always be students to train, and a hospital, as there will always be sick people to treat. On his death he left $7 million in the hands of his trustees to be divided between these two institutions which were to perpetuate his name.

On Tuesday 7th May 1889, the formal opening of the new hospital took place. Responsibility for organising the clinics rested primarily on Osler's shoulders. From the beginning he concentrated on taking students to the bedside for clinical teaching. The original faculty consisted of 'The Big Four', of whom Osler was the second to be appointed after William Welch, a physician and pathologist, who had first studied classics at Yale before moving to Columbia University to study medicine.

Osler then brought Kelly, a gynaecological surgeon, from the University of Pennsylvania Medical School, and Halsted, a general surgeon and graduate of Yale, who had earlier shown that cocaine when injected into a nerve could produce safe and effective local anaesthesia. Sadly Halsted became addicted to cocaine and then morphine, which led to long

*Johns Hopkins*

absences from work, and much of his operating was done by his senior resident Harvey Cushing (later a famous neurosurgeon and Osler's first biographer). Halsted was also responsible for introducing gloves into surgery after giving Caroline Hampton, his first scrub nurse, a pair of gloves to protect her hands – he subsequently married her! Osler was 39, Welsh 38, Halsted 37, and Kelly only 31.

Throughout his life Osler enjoyed practical jokes, often using the pseudonym 'Egerton Yorrick Davis', which occasionally got him into trouble. Two years before he arrived at Hopkins he had conned a respectable medical journal into printing the obscure medical findings of Egerton Yorrick Davis, supposedly a retired Army surgeon who had set up practice in Canada. When the editor discovered the true facts he refused to publish any of Osler's legitimate work – or even to believe it. While Osler's jokes did not always backfire, plenty of people failed to see the funny side. These included some unsuspecting women as they waited nervously for their appointments with the newly arrived Dr Kelly. "You are in the most capable hands," Osler would assure each of them, "and don't worry, old Kelly's senile tremor disappears as soon as it's time to operate." Doubt, then puzzlement would cross their faces when in walked the young gynaecologist.

By the end of its first year Johns Hopkins had 220 beds, and 788 patients had been seen for a total of 15,000 days of treatment. Sixteen years later, when Osler left for Oxford, over 4,200 patients had been seen for a total of nearly 110,000 days of treatment.

All students were expected to do some work in the bacteriology laboratory. Osler also introduced the German postgraduate training system, instituting one year of general

*We are here to add what we can to life, not to get what we can from it.*

internship followed by several years of residency with increasing clinical responsibilities, the basis of which remains in virtually every medical school around the world to this day. He started a journal club and advised:

> *The student practitioner requires at least three things with which to stimulate and maintain his education: a notebook, the library, and the quinquennial brain dusting.*

These were three things that he continued to make use of for the rest of his life. He made it clear to his students and medical audiences that knowledge and wisdom were not the same, often quoting the English poet, William Cowper:

> *Knowledge and wisdom, far from being one,*
> *Have oft-times no connection. Knowledge dwells*
> *In heads replete with thoughts of other men;*
> *Wisdom in minds attentive to their own.*
> *Knowledge is proud that he has learned so much;*
> *Wisdom is humble that he knows no more.*

In May and June 1880 he was again in Europe visiting a number of clinics, but he also was able to attend the famous Passion Play at Oberammergau which has been performed every 10 years since 1634 (although now in years that end with a zero) in gratitude for their deliverance from the bubonic plague.

Back in London he was walking past a boot makers in the West End one day with a colleague when he stopped, entered, and went up to the proprietor, slapped him on the back and

---

*He who studies medicine without books sails an uncharted sea, but he who studies medicine without patients does not go to sea at all.*

exclaimed: "Hello old boy – how have you been all this time?!" The old boy had been his boot maker when he first came to work in London in the early 1870s, and the meeting was like two old friends seeing each other. Visiting other friends at Croxley Green one afternoon he spent several hours carving 'WO' on a beech tree, initials which were still clearly visible in 1921.

*Diseases that harm require treatments that harm less.*

# CHAPTER 8:
# THE PRINCIPLES AND PRACTICE OF MEDICINE

Back at Johns Hopkins the larger part of 1891 was given over to writing his magnum opus: *The Principles and Practice of Medicine*. It was a beautifully written textbook, and notable among its competitors for outlining the futility of most drug therapies of the age. The most influential general medical text for the next 40 years, it was translated into French, German, Spanish and Chinese, with several hundred thousand copies sold. Yet it was to lay a huge burden on him, as it needed revision and updating every three years for the rest of his life.

*Writing the Principles and Practice of Medicine, c. 1891*

He describes a week while he was writing this book in 1891:

*Three mornings of each week I stayed at home and dictated from 8am to 1pm. On alternate days I dictated after the morning hospital visit beginning about 11:30am. The spare hours of the afternoon were devoted to correction and reference work. Early in May I gave up the house and went to my rooms in the hospital, where the routine was similar. After 5pm I saw my outside cases. Dinner at the club about 6.30pm. I loafed until 9.30pm, bed 10pm, up at 7am. During the summer the entire manuscript was carefully revised and the last three months of 1891 were devoted to proof reading. In January I made out the index... and in the internal work nothing so wearied me as the verification of every reference. I was aided by assistants and during the writing of the work I lost only one afternoon through indisposition and never a night's rest. Between September 1890 and January 1892 I gained nearly eight pounds in weight.*

When Osler moved in to the hospital in May, Hunter Robb, Kelly's resident, happened to be in possession of the largest and quietest suite situated at one end of the corridor. Dr Robb recalls:

*Osler asked if I would loan him the use of my library for half an hour or so in the mornings and of course I said, "Yes, with pleasure." The first morning he appeared with one book under his arm accompanied by his stenographer, Miss Humpton. When the morning's work was over he left the book on the library shelf wide*

*There is no more difficult art to acquire than the art of observation, and for some men it is quite as difficult to record an observation in brief and plain language.*

*open. The next morning he brought two books with him, and so on for the next two weeks so that the table and all the chairs and the sofa and the piano and even the floor were covered with open books. As a consequence I was never able to use the room for six months. Often times, right in the middle of his dictation, he would stop, and rushing to my other room asked me to match quarters with him or we would engage in an exchange of yarns. It was a great treat for me and, except when he would gain inspiration by kicking my wastepaper basket about the room, I thoroughly enjoyed his visits.*

Apparently Dr Robb cured him of his habit of kicking the waste paper basket by weighing it down one day with concealed bricks!

Osler dedicated his Magnum Opus in 1892:

To the
Memory of my Teachers:

William Arthur Johnson
Priest of the Parish of Weston, Ontario.

James Bovell
of the Toronto School of Medicine, and of the
University of Trinity College, Toronto.

Robert Palmer Howard
Dean of the Medical Faculty and Professor of Medicine,
McGill University, Montréal

*The young physician starts life with 20 drugs for each disease, and the old physician ends life with one drug for 20 diseases.*

He left a copy in Hunter Robb's room with the following dedication:

> *This book was conceived in robbery and brought forth in fraud. In the spring of 1891 I coolly entered in and took possession of the working room of Dr Hunter Robb. As in the old story of the cuckoo and the hedge sparrow, I just turned him out of his comfortable nest, splattered his floor with pamphlets, papers and trash, and played the devil generally with his comfort.*

He signed it with his 'alter ego':

> *On behalf of the author EYD 4/21/92.*

It was not long before 23,000 copies of the first edition of his textbook were sold – a remarkable record for a medical publication.

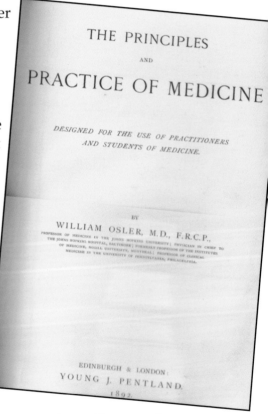

THE PRINCIPLES

AND

PRACTICE OF MEDICINE

DESIGNED FOR THE USE OF PRACTITIONERS AND STUDENTS OF MEDICINE.

BY

WILLIAM OSLER, M.D., F.R.C.P.,
PROFESSOR OF MEDICINE IN THE JOHNS HOPKINS UNIVERSITY; PHYSICIAN IN CHIEF TO THE JOHNS HOPKINS HOSPITAL, BALTIMORE; FORMERLY PROFESSOR OF THE INSTITUTES OF MEDICINE, McGILL UNIVERSITY, MONTREAL; PROFESSOR OF CLINICAL MEDICINE IN THE UNIVERSITY OF PENNSYLVANIA, PHILADELPHIA.

EDINBURGH & LONDON:
YOUNG J. PENTLAND.
1892.

*Observe, record, tabulate, communicate. Use your five senses. Learn to see, learn to hear, learn to feel, learn to smell, and know that by practice alone you can become expert.*

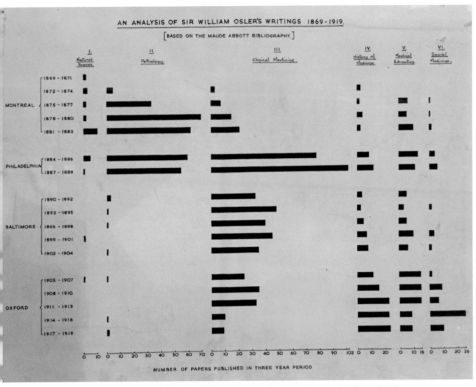

*An analysis of Sir William Osler's writings, 1869-1919*

*No bubble is so iridescent or floats longer
than that blown by the successful teacher.*

# CHAPTER 9: MARRIAGE

Grace Gross (née Revere) was born in Boston in 1854. William had known her since that first invitation to Sunday lunch when he moved to Philadelphia, and had continued to be in communication following the death of Samuel Gross. Someone had warned Grace – perhaps Osler himself – that she was going to marry a man who had books all over the floor. Some months later he spoke about the wife whose life is rendered miserable by a man of books where the dining room table is covered, whose house is never cleared, and to whom time had no meaning and could breakfast at five o'clock in the evening and dine on the following day.

Osler's textbook was published on 24th February 1892, and on that day with a copy under his arm, Osler is reported to have entered the house of mutual friends in Baltimore where Mrs Gross was staying. He threw the volume into her lap with the words, "There, take the darn thing! Now what are you going to do with the man?" The families were told of the proposed wedding in April.

Early in May Osler spoke at the second annual dinner of the Johns Hopkins residents' association, and the following Saturday took a train to Philadelphia, where he called at 1112 Walnut Street, the home of Grace. Here a former colleague, James Wilson, happened to turn up and found him sitting under a tree in the garden with Mrs Gross. Wilson asked, "Hello Osler, what are you doing here? Won't you come and have lunch with me?" "No," replied Osler, "I am lunching here; why don't you stay?" This he did, and over lunch they spoke about moose hunting and fishing in the salmon rivers. Presently Mrs Gross asked to be excused with the statement that she was going out in a hansom cab. She waited by the door, whereupon Wilson left and Osler said that Mrs Gross would give him a lift as she was going in his direction. It was not until then that her devoted servant Margaret was told by her mistress that she was going to be married at 2:30pm, and the faithful girl, taken totally by surprise, exclaimed, "...and only in the *hansom*, ma'am?!"

Leaving their bags at the station they drove to Saint James's Church where the ceremony was performed and, having walked back to the train station, Osler sent a telegram to Wilson saying:

> *It was awfully kind of you to come to the wedding breakfast!*

They began their honeymoon in New York and then travelled to Toronto, Montreal and on to Boston where they were warmly received by Osler's professional friends and both their families. At the end of May they sailed for Southampton. Osler had written to a friend in England saying, "You will like Mrs Osler very much; she is an old friend of mine. I feel very safe."

July was passed in Devon and Cornwall visiting an aunt in Falmouth, but William attended the British Medical Association meeting in Nottingham, an occasion which gave his new wife such distaste for these functions that her advice to other medical wives was to keep away from them: "Lest they pass the time darning their husbands socks in a hotel bedroom while he gallivants with his male companions!"

*Medicine is a science of uncertainty and an art of probability.*

Back in Baltimore he found a house that was on the market, 1 West Franklin Street, and having put his head inside the front door he made an offer without further investigation, which was accepted. He said to his wife that it reminded him of her house 1112 Walnut Street, Philadelphia. This remained their home while in Baltimore and became famous for its hospitality.

By 1890 the Johns Hopkins Hospital had been firmly established, but the university trustees were looking for money to build an undergraduate school. At the same time McGill was trying to get Osler to return – an offer he considered, but in December one donor, Mary Garrett, offered to give $300,000 to complete the $500,000 endowment at Johns Hopkins, on condition that women would be admitted on the same basis as men. When this news arrived, Osler wrote declining the offer to return to his native country and instead put his efforts into the new medical school which was opened in Baltimore.

The Baltimore of the early 1890s was surrounded on the north and west by the beautiful rolling countryside and wooded hills of Maryland to which the well to do moved in the hot summer months. The hospital was on a hill on the outskirts of the city to the east. Number 1 West Franklin Street was near the cathedral, about two miles away from the hospital. A 'bob-tailed horse car', one of the classic early street cars, made its tortuous way through the untidy cobbled streets and would toil slowly up the hill east or west with an extra horse attached for the hill climb. Baths and refuse from houses, factories and tanneries, emptied into the gutters of the cobbled streets, and stepping stones prevented the population from dirtying their feet.

*It is much simpler to buy books than to read them and easier to read them than to absorb their contents.*

*Professor and Mrs Osler on their first visit to Oxford, August 1894*

In February 1893 a son was born to the Oslers, but he lived for only a few days. With his usual attempt to mask his feelings said, "I whistle that I may not weep." But with a desire to console his wife for her sadness, he sent her a letter full of tenderness, purporting to come from their baby in heaven from describing his happy surroundings and begging his mother not to worry.

In the summer of 1894 he attended the British Medical Association in Bristol, and then went to Oxford for the British Association for the Advancement of Science where he met up with John Burdon Sanderson and Sir Henry Acland, the Regius Professor of Medicine. Acland was described as a man of enlightened mind and a "strenuous fighter against the academic powers of darkness", in comparison with one of his predecessors who, being shown a delicate preparation under a microscope, declared first that he did not believe it, and secondly, that if it were true he did not think God meant us to know it.

It was in Acland's library that Osler first saw the panel above the mantelpiece with the three portraits of Linacre, Harvey and Sydenham. Linacre was a literary physician who was responsible for the revival of Greek learning in England in the sixteenth century. Harvey was a leading physician and experimental scientist who was the first to describe the circulation of the blood in his classic work, *De Motu Cordis,* and Sydenham was a model physician and undisputed master of the English medical world. Such was his delight with it that Grace Osler asked Sir Henry if he would arrange to get a copy for Osler as a birthday present. He agreed, and in due course the picture adorned the mantelpiece of his own office in Baltimore and became a familiar sight to countless students,

*Varicose veins are the result of an improper selection of grandparents.*

*Linacre, Harvey and Sydenham on the mantelpiece at Norham Gardens*

friends and patients. It moved with him to Oxford and remains to this day in 13 Norham Gardens.

By 1894 Johns Hopkins had 50 undergraduates and there was a more intimate group among the junior house staff who had free access to Osler's house at any time. These were known as the 'latch-keyers', each having a key to the door. Osler would also give a plain gold ring to some of these 'latch-key' staff, so that when they travelled to the continent for their medical studies it might protect them from any young lady who had designs on them.

The year 1895 ended happily for on 28th December his son was born. This was a particular joy for them both, having lost their first son. He was given the name Revere after his wife's great-grandfather Paul Revere, who had died in 1818 and had been a patriot in the American Revolution, best known for a

*To confess ignorance is often wiser than to beat*
*about the bush with a hypothetical diagnosis.*

memorable midnight ride to Lexington to warn New England towns of the approach of the British. Longfellow dramatised this in the 1861 poem, 'Paul Revere's Ride' (see appendix 1).

Osler was always devoted to his son, and after Revere's birth he brought all his medical friends up to look at him. He called him a variety of names over the years, sometimes referring him as 'Tommy', 'Isaac', 'Ike' or 'Egerton Junior'.

*Osler with Revere as a young boy*

*Start at once a bedside library and spend the last half hour of the day in communion with the saints of humanity.*

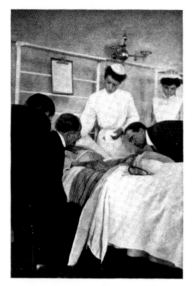

Inspection

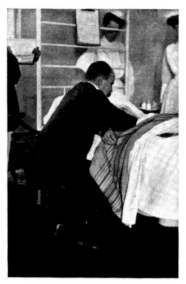

Palpation

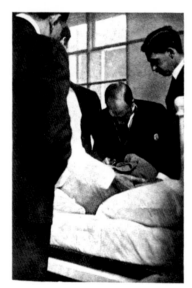

Auscultation

Contemplation

*Osler at the bedside*
*Snapshots by TW Clarke*

# CHAPTER 10: TEACHING

Each morning as he walked down the hospital corridor the students would gather around him, and by time the ward was reached the group had generally grown to a small avalanche. Osler took the students to the bedside. He called it the natural method of teaching – the student begins with the patient, continues with the patient, and ends his studies with the patient, using books and lectures as tools and simply as a means to an end. His emphasis was on the method of examination. Then he would summarise the patient's condition and add appropriate illustrations from his reading and experience that helped to fix the facts in the minds of the students.

*Teach him how to observe, look first before touching. Give him plenty of facts to observe and the lessons will come out of the facts themselves. For the junior student in medicine and surgery the best teaching is that taught by the patient himself. The whole art of medicine is in observation. To educate the eye to see, the ear to hear and the finger to feel takes time, and to start a man on the right path is all that we can do. Give the student good methods and the proper point of view, and all other things will be added, as his experience grows.*

He goes on to say:

*The practice of medicine is an art, not a trade; a calling not a business; the calling in which your heart will be exercised equally with your head. Often the best part of your work will have nothing to do with potions and powders, but with the exercise of an influence of the strong upon the weak, of the righteous upon the wicked, the wise upon the foolish. To you, as the trusted family counsellor, the father will come with his anxieties, the mother with her hidden griefs, the daughter with her trials and the son with his follies.... Your courage and cheerfulness will not only carry you over the rough places of life but will also enable you to bring comfort and help to the weak-hearted, and will console you in those same hours when you have to 'whistle that you may not weep'.*

Like every consultant he experienced the anguish of patients he was unable to cure, and would quote Matthew Arnold's wish:

*Nor bring to see me cease to live*
*Some doctor full of praise and fame,*
*To shake his sapient head, and give*
*The ill he cannot cure, a name.*

He goes on to explain how often under such circumstances had the bitterness of the last line occurred to him! Yet he never forgot the patient in his interests about the disease, and there was a tradition among the clinical students that if they wanted to see the chief at his best, watch him as he passed the bedside

*Advice is sought to confirm a position already taken.*

of some poor old soul with a chronic and hopeless malady as, "They always get his best."

One student described how he was called up to Osler's clinic to see a patient and make a diagnosis and found the chief "sitting on the table and swinging his feet and asking all sorts of questions you have never heard of before."

In the winter of 1896 Osler delivered a series of lectures on *angina pectoris*, relating the story of John Hunter's heart attack which ended in his sudden death at St George's Hospital in London following a fit of rage at a board meeting. He also gave instances in which the disease was found in families, one striking example being that of the Arnold family. Thomas Arnold, the famous headmaster of Rugby School, died after his first attack on the eve of his 47th birthday. His father, a Collector of Customs at Cowes on the Isle of Wight, had died of a heart attack in 1801 and his son, Matthew Arnold the poet, died suddenly on 15th April 1888 at the age of 65.

*Study until 25, investigate until 40, profession until 60,*
*at which age I would have him retired on a double allowance.*

*Osler reclining*

# CHAPTER 11: ROCKEFELLER INSTITUTE OF MEDICAL RESEARCH

In the summer of 1897 a Baptist minister, Rev Frederick Gates, who wanted to learn more about medicine, was reading a copy of Osler's textbook in the Catskill Mountains northwest of New York. He also happened to be a member of John D Rockefeller's philanthropic staff. Gates took a medical dictionary to help him understand the book, but he read it from cover to cover and found it to be one of very few scientific books that possessed a high literary quality. In writing *The Principles and Practice of Medicine*, Osler berated the lack of science in medicine as it existed in 1897. Having read it, it became abundantly clear to Gates that medicine would not become a science unless money was available to allow qualified men to engage in scientific research on a salary independent of clinical practice. He suggested to Mr Rockefeller that this was an opportunity for him to become a pioneer in this area if he so wished. After consideration and consultation Mr Rockefeller agreed, and in due course the Rockefeller Institute of Medical Research was set up, having its origins in Osler's textbook. It would be five years before Osler came to hear of Gates' summer reading project.

In August Osler attended the meeting for the British Association for the Advancement of Science, held for only the second time in Canada. It was memorable on two fronts. Firstly there were exceptionally high temperatures, such that the usual frock-coated Englishmen with top hats appeared in the streets in shirtsleeves in an unusually casual way. Secondly it was attended by Lord Lister, who had just been made a peer and was currently President of the Royal Society. The following year Osler was himself elected as a Fellow of the Royal Society and Lister presided at the ceremony in London. It was an honour that had been given to very few Canadians.

The new century dawned and, at the end of January, senior members of Edinburgh University tried to entice Osler to apply for the Chair of Medicine which was soon to become vacant. It was a tempting proposition, especially as both he and his wife wished to have Revere educated in 'the old country'. He hoped he would be invited without having to go through an application process but was told that an invitation was out of the question. Lord Robertson, in answer to a letter from Sir Michael Foster urging Osler's election without the customary formalities, diplomatically replied:

> *I fully believe that to those who know Professor Osler it may seem absurd and superfluous that he should produce testimonials yet your own experience will probably suggest that he must remember that the electors are outside the circle in which even the highest scientific reputations are known and accordingly it would be wise that this tribute be paid to our ignorance.*

In Baltimore he was again the doctor's doctor, and was becoming overwhelmed with appeals for advice from his professional colleagues or members of their families. This, alongside calls to see people of national prominence, was not something he could avoid. This was one of the reasons why he was so tempted by the Chair of Medicine in Edinburgh, as

*The practice of medicine is an art, not a trade; a calling, not a business; a calling in which your heart will be exercised equally with your head.*

it would be a respite from these requests which he was unable to refuse.

Eventually he was persuaded to send in an application, but word got out and 'all hell broke loose in Baltimore', leading to his telegram on 26<sup>th</sup> March saying:

> *Application withdrawn. Local pressure too strong. So sorry. Osler.*

Nevertheless the committee still decided to send him a telegram the day before the election saying that the Chair was his if he would accept it. He did not.

Back in London in the summer he went on the familiar round of activities which included second-hand bookshops and auction sales. Many of his purchases were subsequently given to fill the gaps in the library in Baltimore. He also put his final touches to a promised address to a group of 3,000 medical graduates, speaking on the importance of postgraduate study and recommending it as an antidote to premature senility. He spoke of graduate students of preceding centuries frequenting the fountains of learning in Italy, Holland, Great Britain, France and Austria predicting, quite correctly as it transpired, that in the twentieth century the young English physician would find inspiration in the United States, the "land of the setting sun."

In the summer of 1901 the family were back in Europe, spending a holiday in Ostend where Osler, who had learned his water tricks on the ponds of upper Canada, proceeded to walk around on the floor of the ocean on his hands, waving his legs in the air, to the amazement of the locals and the embarrassment of his wife!

*The Scots are the backbone of Canada.*
*They are all right in their three vital parts – head, heart and haggis.*

Back in London he and Lord Lister were both speaking at the British Congress on Tuberculosis. With 2,500 delegates, the two of them entered together to rapturous applause. Tuberculosis was a disease which had spared no families, whether rich or poor, prince or pauper. The Duke of Cambridge, cousin to Queen Victoria who had died six months previously, graced the meeting. The Duke had served in the Crimean War and asked Osler to sit down and chat to him.

It is possible that he told the Duke about the time when he was a student in Toronto, and how he had on one occasion met an old soldier who had been discharged from the army after the Crimean War for an aneurysm of the aorta. The old man died in 1885 when Osler was at Pennsylvania, and he was given the specimen to draw, describing a saccular aneurysm at the junction of the arch and descending aorta, almost certainly due to syphilis.

Osler often spoke of tuberculosis as captain of the men of death – a phrase he took from the non-conformist preacher and author of *Pilgrim's Progress*, John Bunyan. Osler would add that the captain had now been demoted to lieutenant and would soon be reduced to the ranks, although it was almost too much to expect that he would actually be drummed out of the regiment completely.

In March 1902 Gates met Osler and introduced himself as Mr Rockefeller's representative. It was then that Osler learned for the first time of Gates' summer occupation of 1897, when he had obtained a copy of Osler's textbook and read it from cover to cover. Gates went on to say that, after establishing the Institute, Mr Rockefeller contributed $1 million to the Harvard

*To it, more than to anything else, I owe whatever success I have had – to this power of settling down to the day's work and trying to do it to the best of one's ability, and letting the future take care of itself.*

School, adding that, "Both of these gifts came directly out of your book."

At the meeting of the Hopkins Medical Society in November 1902, Osler showed an example of the condition of cyanosis with polycythaemia in which he had come to take special interest. It has since become coupled with his name as Osler's Disease.

*Nothing in life is more wonderful than faith – the one great moving force which we can neither weigh in the balance nor test in the crucible.*

# CHAPTER 12: THE OXFORD CALL

In 1904 Sir John Burdon Sanderson announced his intention to resign as the Regius Professor of Medicine in Oxford due to ill health. The Oxford graduates had held a meeting in London in January, and in a letter to *The Times* said that a physician who is representative of medicine in its widest sense should be invited as the Regius Professor of Medicine.

The chair came with a small allowance of £400 a year, and many wondered if they would find a man willing to forgo the financial rewards to which his abilities entitled him. The President of the Royal College of Physicians and the Vice-Chancellor of Oxford University were involved in the selection, but the Regius Professor is a crown appointment created by Henry VIII in 1546. It was rumoured that Mr Balfour the Prime Minister might take the matter out of the hands of the contending parties and offer an independent nomination to the King. It is not clear who first put forward Osler's name, as a number of local physicians were also contenders for the post, but two names outside the Oxford Circle had been suggested to the Prime Minister – Sir Patrick Manson, a British parasitologist who founded the field of tropical medicine, and William Osler.

Osler himself was taken up by other activities in the first part of the year, not only in a number of conferences, but more poignantly he arrived back from Washington on 7ᵗʰ February to find the business section of Baltimore in flames. The fire came within two blocks of his home in West Franklin Street, and the household was packed and ready to leave as brands of fire were falling on roofs in the neighbourhood. However, the high winds which had been blowing from the south all day shifted and by 2.00 am they were told that there was no further danger. From this devastating fire a newer and better Baltimore arose, although for a time many individuals and institutions were hard-hit. Among them was the Johns Hopkins Hospital, for many of the properties it owned, and from which it obtained rent, had been destroyed by the fire.

In Oxford it seems that John Burdon Sanderson had received a letter from the Prime Minister mentioning Osler's name. Sanderson had not initially considered his former pupil because of his refusal to take the Edinburgh chair, but no sooner was his name mentioned than Sanderson clapped his hand to his forehead and said, "That's it! The very man!"

In June 1904 Sanderson wrote to Osler saying

> *I think I should add that my only reason for resigning my post is that declining ill health and strength make me unable to do the work efficiently. As you'll see from the papers sent by this post, the work is very light. The Regius Professor need not reside in Oxford more than one third of the year, so that he can, if he likes, avail himself of the proximity of London for any work or purpose that may require his presence.*

In June, Grace Osler had taken Revere to Canada where they had rented a cottage at Murray Bay for the summer. They never paid much attention to family birthdays so she was surprised to hear that Osler was planning to arrive on Sunday morning in time for her birthday. A twinkle in his eye when

*Care more for the individual patient than for the special features of the disease. Put yourself in his place, the kindly word, the cheerful greeting, the sympathetic look – these the patient understands.*

they met told her that something was afoot. As he sat in the back seat of the carriage with her, he handed Sanderson's letter to her with a finger over his mouth urging her not to make an exclamation of surprise. Osler wrote back saying that he would like to be considered for the post:

> *I feel overworked and am finding it increasingly hard to serve the public and carry on my teaching. I have been in harness actively for 30 years, and have been looking forward to the time when I could ease myself of some of the burdens that I carry at present.*

With the income from his book they had no financial worries, and the stipend of £400 would not be the problem that it might have been for others. His only doubts were the lack of clinical bedside teaching, and he goes on to say:

> *I should miss sadly the daily contact with the students, unless I could arrange for clinical work in London.*

His wife, in a later letter to William's mother, commented:

> *As I read the letter (from Sanderson) I felt a tremendous weight lifted from my shoulders as I had become very anxious about the danger of his keeping on with the pace he had been going on for several years in Baltimore.*

In spite of the fact that he often said his ideal of life would be to live within an hour of the British Museum and to have *The Times* on his breakfast table, and commenting years before after visiting the city that, "I have lost my heart to Oxford",

---

*Medicine is learned by the bedside and not in the classroom. Let not your conceptions of disease come from words heard in the lecture room or read from the book. See, and then reason and compare and control. But see first.*

he had difficulty in coming to a decision when he was officially offered the post in July. And so it was that he wrote to his wife from London expressing uncertainty. She was still in Canada and received his letter one Sunday morning. She read it, went straight away to the telegraph office and cabled: "Do not procrastinate accept at once."

He showed this to several friends and folded the telegram over so that they only saw the words 'Do not procrastinate' and they were unsure whether 'accept' or 'refuse' was the next word!

Balfour's official letter written on behalf of the King asking him to take the Chair reached him on 5th August, the day before he sailed for America. He accepted with the request that the facts were not to be made known for two weeks.

Back in Baltimore he gave three valedictory addresses, including one entitled 'The Fixed Period' which landed him in trouble, when he suggested the uselessness of men above 60 years of age, and the incalculable benefit it would be if men stopped work at this age. The title was taken from Anthony Trollope's novel where a plot hinges on admission to a college at which men retired at the age of 60 for a year of contemplation before a peaceful departure by chloroform, thus avoiding the calamities which many will experience during the seventh and eighth decades. This attempt at jocularity failed when the American press sensationalised the story, claiming that Osler had seriously recommended that all older persons be chloroformed. Nothing could have been further from Osler's mind. He was deeply hurt by the uproar, which also resulted in the cancellation of plans to commemorate his name in Baltimore. The verb 'to oslerise' had a brief vogue as a synonym for 'to kill by chloroforming'!

*Courage and cheerfulness will not only carry you over the rough places in life, but will enable you to bring comfort and help to the weak-hearted and will console you in the sad hours.*

10 Downing Street
Whitehall SW

5 August 1904

10 Downing Street
Whitehall SW

Confidential
5 August 1904
Dictated

My dear Sir

I have the permission of the
King to propose to you the
appointment to the vacant
Chair of Medicine in the
University of Oxford. I am
satisfied that your selection
will command the formal
approval of the University
and of all those interested in
the advancement of Medical
science, and I sincerely trust
that you will find yourself
able to give a favourable
reply to this invitation which
I have the honour to address
to you.

I am sir
Yours Sincerely

Arthur James Balfour

*In science the credit goes to the man who convinces the world, not to the
man to whom the idea first occurs.*

Before his departure for Oxford he finished the revision for the 6th edition of his textbook, and on 19ᵗʰ May 1905 they sailed from New York on *The Cedric*, arriving in Oxford on Saturday evening of 27ᵗʰ May where they took up rented lodgings in 7 Norham Gardens, fully furnished and owned by Mrs Muller. Her husband, Professor Max Muller, was a Sanskrit specialist and one of the founders of the western academic field of Indian studies and comparative religion who had died five years previously. Osler was totally exhausted, and it was six weeks before he felt himself again.

*The golden rule of Confucius quoted by Sir Thomas Browne –*
*it is a wise rule to take the world as we find it, not always to leave it so.*

# CHAPTER 13: OXFORD

No transition could have been greater, from a noisy Baltimore and the hurly-burly of the preceding month, to a quiet Oxford suburb where they were kept awake by the wood pigeons cooing on the chimney. From a sweltering Maryland to an English spring time, which that year was so cold that they promptly built a fire in the dining room that greatly shocked the warmly-dressed Oxonians who first dropped in on them.

His wife was very happy. The house was charming with a little lawn, broad flowerbeds, shrubs and trees looking into the University Parks with the lilacs, laburnum and hawthorn in blossom.

The senior Oxford chairs have automatic college attachments, and as Regius he had had offers of college fellowships from Oriel, Lincoln and New College but accepted one at Christ Church, where the fellows are called students! The Regius chair remains linked to Christ Church to this day. From the early seventeenth century the Regius Professor of Medicine in Oxford has also been Master of Ewelme Almshouses, situated in a village of the same name 16 miles south of Oxford, providing an excuse for a delightful trip into the Oxfordshire countryside.

Three of their early visitors were his recent colleagues from Baltimore, Welch, Halsted and Kelly. On 9th June all were in London at John Singer Sargent's studio for the first sitting of the now famous portrait of the four of them. Sargent was an

*The Almshouses*
  *at Ewelme*

*As Regius Professor, Osler was Master of the Almshouses in Ewelme*

*We are here not to get all we can out of life for ourselves but to try to make the lives of others happier. This is the essence of the admonition of Christ – he that finds his life shall lose it and he that loses his life, for my sake, shall find it.*

American artist who was considered to be the leading portrait painter of his generation, and he had settled in London. He took a lot of trouble at the outset with the grouping of these four. Welch's head and his blue beard were almost completed at the first sitting, and the book he is supposed to be reading is a seventeenth century edition of Petrarch. Osler's likeness gave him the greatest trouble and was scraped out and done again. Sargent became discouraged over his composition and finally brought an old Venetian globe from another studio which required part of the casing to be chipped away before it would fit though the door. Welch had asked Sargent if he might wear his Yale robe and the painter acquiesced, but when Osler spoke of wearing his red Oxford robe Sargent said:

*No, I can't paint you in that: I know all about that red – they gave me a degree down there and I've got one of those robes. I've left it on the roof in the rain and I've buried it in the garden. It's no use, the red is as red as ever, the stuff is too good, it won't fade. Now if you can get a Dublin degree the red robes are made of different stuff and if you wash them they come down to a beautiful pink!*

By September the picture was finished and Osler was pleased with it saying,

*Welch is very good but I do not like Halsted or Kelly, and Halsted says mine is awful but I think that when looked at from a distance it will be a good representation.*

*Errors in judgement must occur in the practice of an art which consists largely in balancing probabilities.*

69

*John Singer Sargent's 'The Four Doctors'.*
*From left to right: Welch, Halsted, Osler and Kelly.*

He made an early visit to Cambridge where he met his counterpart, Sir Clifford Allbutt, the inventor of the clinical thermometer, and on a subsequent meeting in London they arrived at a reception together and Osler whispered a word into the ear of the usher, who then announced in a loud voice, "The brothers Regii!" and they entered together and made a low bow.

In the autumn the new edition of the textbook was printed and number 100,000 was given to Revere. He soon had 15 students to teach at the Radcliffe Infirmary where there were 150 beds and a large outpatient department. Although the medical students completed their clinical training in London, many of them would travel to Oxford on a Sunday where Osler took rounds at the Radcliffe Infirmary. As Regius he had access to all the patients there. He also had rooms at Christ Church, rooms in the Museum and was made a curator at the Bodleian which, with his love of books, was a source of great joy and industry.

*Out-patients of the Radcliffe Infirmary before development in 1863*

*In the life of a young man the most essential thing for happiness is the gift of friendship.*

## The Bodleian Library

In 1444, the existing university library in Oxford had been augmented by a gift of some 300 manuscripts from the Duke of Gloucester, youngest son of Henry IV. This prompted the university to build the beautiful library above the Divinity School that bears his name, The Duke Humfrey Library. During the Reformation of the 1550s, the library had been stripped and abandoned, remaining virtually untouched until Sir Thomas Bodley rescued it in 1598. He was a Fellow of Merton College and in the diplomatic service of Queen Elizabeth I. Bodley had married a rich widow, whose first husband had made a fortune trading in pilchards, and on his retirement from the affairs of state, Bodley restored the library which now bears his name.

From 1860 to 1906 there had been little to note in the history of the library but then in 1906, shortly after Osler's arrival, the situation changed. The first entry of that year was recovery of an original copy of the first folio of Shakespeare which had initially come to the library in 1623, and had been removed after the restoration of the monarchy. It was bought back by a public donation of £3,000.

In April the Oslers bought 13 Norham Gardens (built in the 1870s) but due to alterations it was January 1907 before they moved in. From then on it became known as the 'Open Arms', renowned throughout the rest of their lives for its hospitality for which the Oslers were famed.

In Baltimore he had had plenty of help with strong university backing but in Oxford he was engaged almost single-handedly in putting some life into the much-neglected Oxford School of Medicine. No contrast could have been greater. Even as late as the seventeenth century, little had been

*Typhoid fever is the index of sanitation.*

required of the Regius Professor of Medicine in Oxford, apart from reading a lecture to whoever cared to listen twice a week on the text of Hippocrates and Galen. There was also one dissection each year conducted during Lent by the reader in anatomy – if the execution of a criminal occurred at a suitable time!

In December 1906 Osler was back in Canada for his mother's 100th birthday and there were countless messages and telegrams, including one from the Archbishop of Canterbury. During the day she recounted how in 1815, as a young child of nine, she walked all the way from Hampstead to Bushy Park to carry the news of the victory at the Battle of Waterloo. She had lived during the reign of five monarchs. George III and IV, William, Victoria and Edward. She had six living children, 26 grandchildren and 21 great-grandchildren. She died three months later when Osler was back in Oxford, and in his usual fashion he showed little emotion to his friends over her death.

A friend who knew him said his pose of impert-urbability was purely a defensive mechanism. He described Osler as a quiet young man who always had

*Ellen Free Osler at the age of one hundred*

*Jaundice is the disease that your friends diagnose.*

Oct 31d.

7, NORHAM GARDENS,
OXFORD.

Dear Mrs Parmelee

It was
a great disappointment
to me not to be able to
get away this summer,
but we had the usual
worries incident to remodelling
a new house & I could not
get the contracts arranged
in time to leave.
Your faithful Whitlemmas
report from Feb. to Sept

7th & most satisfactory. It
is the longest period you
have passed without an
attack. I dare say the dizzy-
spells will gradually become
less frequent. Your farm
accounts are most interesting.
How happy you must be
over it all! I have been
looking over the farm
records of an old Hospital
of which I am a Officer
the Master & which our
farm accounts go back to
1343. They wish to know
the price of a pig in 1400
or of a calf in 1505 I
can tell you to a farthing

We sail Nov 28th in
return about the ____ again early
in January. My Mother's 100th birthday is on
Dec 14th & of course we are all looking forward
to the event with the greatest interest. Let
me know at the Johns Hopkins Hospital when
you expect to be in N.Y. or in Washington.
With kind regards to Mrs Parmelee & your
father & ____.

sincerely yours
W Osler

Thank Miss Whitlemmas for
the good report.

Dear Mrs Parmelee

It was a great disappointment to me not to be able to get away this summer but we have had the usual worries incident to remodelling a new house and I could not get the contracts arranged in time to leave.

Your faithful (medical) report from Feb. to Sept 7th is most satisfactory. It is the longest period you have passed without an attack. I dare say the dizzy spells will gradually become less frequent. Your farm accounts are most interesting. How happy you must be over it all! I have been looking over the farm records of an old hospital for which I am ex officio the Master and for which our farm accounts go back to 1393. If you wish to know the price of a pig in 1400 or for a calf in 1505 I can tell you to a farthing. We sail on Nov 28th on the Celtic I hope to be in Baltimore about 10th December and again early in January. My mother's 100th birthday is on Dec 14th and of course we are all looking forward to the event with the greatest interest. Let them know at the Johns Hopkins Hospital when you expect to be in N.Y.or in Washington. With kind regards to Mr Parmelee and your father and mother.

Sincerely Yours
Wm Osler
Thank (doctor) For a good report.

*Letter written by Osler which makes*
*reference to his mother's 100th birthday*

*13 Norham Gardens*
 *'The Open Arms'*

the same serious manner, with unperturbed features and an almost expressionless face such that strangers were entirely unprepared for the humour that would sally forth. This would often come at unexpected times without any change in countenance, but in a similar vein he hid his emotion to others when bereaved. He always had the deepest philosophical interest in death, but when death touched him personally, although he suffered deeply he never permitted others to see it, and brushed his sorrow and it's emotions aside saying, "If I laugh at any mortal thing t'is that I may not weep."

Osler played a major part in starting the Oxford University endowment funds and £150,000 was collected during 1907. Much of that money was spent on the School of Engineering, a new clinical laboratory and in the construction of the underground storage chamber for the Bodleian Library.

In June he was involved in the inauguration of the Royal Society of Medicine (RSM) which brought together twenty of the older medical societies in London, and he was active securing a new building at 1 Wimpole Street. Five years later he started the history of medicine section. Later in life he was invited to become President of the RSM, but despite serious pressure he refused to be persuaded, much to the disquiet of the committee. For the first time in its history the RSM had departed from the tradition which demanded that the presidents should be 'the best of those who have served the longest'. The letter of invitation to him finished, "It is your clear duty to accept, and you must not refuse." But refuse he did, writing, "Awfully sorry I cannot accept the nomination. It is not my job. I need not go into reasons. It is good of you to think of me. Sincerely yours."

*Do not waste the hours of daylight in*
*listening to that which you may read by night.*

The Oxford clinical school did not start until the 1960s. Before that the students would complete their undergraduate training in Oxford and move to London for their clinical training, although they returned to Oxford to take their final examination. Examining for medical finals in 1907, one student described how Dr Osler seemed as anxious for them all to pass as a close relative would be, and bending over one patient on which a full clinical report was asked for, the candidate would find the Regius Professor at his elbow with his hand over the patient's heart saying, "A good thrill that – a nice case to have!" – and he then passed on.

At the end of June every year in Oxford the Encaenia procession takes place, when the Vice-Chancellor and leading academics process to the Sheldonian theatre for the awarding of honorary degrees. 1906 had seen an unprecedented turn out from the inhabitants of Oxford to see the academic procession as Rudyard Kipling and Samuel Langhorne Clemens (better known as Mark Twain) were to receive honorary degrees. The Kaiser had also received an honorary degree that year, although that was given to him at Windsor, and Osler accompanied Lister to Windsor for that ceremony.

Osler was susceptible to attacks of bronchitis, and a succession of colds were not helped by the damp Oxford weather and the cold rooms of the old university buildings where many meetings were held. He wrote all his afflictions down in the notebook he invariably kept in his pocket.

In every letter he wrote to friends or family, he spoke of his son who was enjoying Lynam's School in Bardwell Road (now known as the Dragon School) and becoming a first class cricketer. He was twelve and already as tall as his father, but

*Don't touch the patient – state first what you see;*
*cultivate your powers of observation.*

unlike his father he was not much of a student but more interested in butterflies, fish and other wildlife.

By this time the motorcar was in use and although it was not a form of transport in which Grace Osler took great pleasure, it did make it easy to reach otherwise inaccessible places and occasionally the Oslers used it for longer trips. When the car would not start one day, the chauffeur recommended a young Oxford mechanic by the name of William Morris who worked through the night to fix it, allowing Osler to be driven to an important rural consultation the following day. Morris became the family mechanic and when the car would not start Osler would 'send for Willy'. In turn Osler became William's physician when he suffered from his various ailments. After making his fortune as a manufacturer of motorcars, William Morris (later Lord Nuffield) became one of Oxford's greatest medical benefactors, perhaps in memory of Osler.

Osler was one of the John Radcliffe Trustees responsible for managing the doctor's estate. Amongst the other Trustees were the Chancellor of Oxford University and the Archbishop of Canterbury. Each year the trust funded the Radcliffe Travelling Fellowships, and Osler was often involved in the selection.

Some aspects of college life in Oxford, in which William Osler was now immersed, had changed little over the centuries. He described the snuff taken in the common rooms of the colleges from the middle of the seventeenth century as, "Too good a custom to be allowed to lapse," adding, "My good friend Harvey, a don of 80 summers, carries three snuffboxes."

*In taking a history follow each line of thought; ask no leading questions; never suggest. Give the patient's own words in the complaint.*

He was asked to stand as Rector of Edinburgh University and came third in the vote to Wyndham who had been Secretary of State for Ireland and was elected. Churchill just beat him into second place, but Osler had achieved a measure of success never before attained by any non-political candidate at that time.

And so it was that in the October of 1908 Osler went for his 'quinquennial brain-dusting' to the continent. In Bologna he was allowed to scour the University library and the local museum to which his position as curator of the Bodleian gave him ready access. In Venice he wrote to a friend in Baltimore that he had sent him a reproduction of an Avicenna manuscript, having seen the wonderfully illustrated original in Bologna. Avicenna was a Persian physician born in 980 AD, regarded as one of the most significant thinkers and writers of the Islamic Golden Age and whose *Canon of Medicine* remains a medical classic. He also managed to send a first edition of *De Humani Corporis Fabrica*, to the Frick library in Baltimore, one of the most influential books on human anatomy written by the sixteenth century physician, Vesalius.

In many of his lectures he stressed the importance of having hobbies outside medicine regardless of what they were, although he always made a special plea for the pleasant paths of bibliography, and he emphasised the importance of reading as part of postgraduate study saying that,

> *The average non-reading doctor might play a good game of golf or of bridge but professionally is a lost soul! The driven and tired practitioner might plead that he could not find time to read. Those who formed the practising of reading in less busy days will find that the habit of*

*I have learned since to be a better student,*
*and to be ready to say to my fellow students, "I do not know".*

*reading is more likely to continue. It is easier to buy books than to read them and easier to read them than to absorb them.*

Osler bought books and read them, not always with the support of his wife who thought some of the books he bought were an expensive indulgence. So much so that he had a hidden compartment constructed in one of the bookcases in Norham Gardens where he secreted away newly acquired books from Lady Osler.

*The hidden book compartment!*

In 1910 the Radcliffe Infirmary determined to devote certain hours of its outpatient department each week to the treatment of those with consumption (tuberculosis), coming from all parts of the district. This would mean a large increase in the work of the Infirmary and the Oxford County Association for the prevention of tuberculosis, although Osler promised to make good any deficits incurred. He was involved in the management of tuberculosis outside Oxford and often visited the sanatorium at Midhurst in Sussex opened in 1906 by King Edward VII, still in operation in the 1950s when the author's father-in-law was a patient there.

*The best thing nature can do with gallstones is to close the stone quarry and shutdown the business.*

*Osler's study at Norham Gardens*

In Oxford Dr James Murray was one of Osler's patients. For 20 years he had been compiling the Oxford English Dictionary. The first volume appeared in 1888 and one day as he observed Murray emerging from the Old Ashmolean where the work was in progress Osler was heard to remark, "The University pays me my salary to keep that old man alive until his 80th birthday in 1917 when the dictionary will be finished." Sadly Murray died in 1915 and the dictionary took a few more years to complete.

*There is no higher ambition than to become an all round family doctor, whose business in life is to know disease and to know how to treat it.*

1910 also found Osler laid up with a recurrence of ureteric colic due to a small stone from the kidney trying to pass down the ureter to the bladder. He had suffered this affliction since Baltimore days and described how he finally managed to pass the stone after, "A week of squirming, feeling a bit shaken but otherwise well." He was obviously pleased to avoided the surgeon's knife, which would have been the case had he not passed the stone. However, always the joker, he sent a pebble from his garden to the Professor of Chemistry to analyse, pretending it was the stone that he had passed.

He was due to give the celebrated Romanes Lecture in May at the personal invitation of the Vice-Chancellor. Endowed in 1891 by John Romanes of Christ Church, this annual lecture was first given by William Gladstone in 1892. However it was postponed due to the death of King Edward VII on 6th May 1910. Osler remarked that, "It is awfully sad about the king but at 69 a short sharp illnesses was a mercy", and he went on to add, "King George (V) will be alright – he seems a very sensible fellow."

When he finally gave the lecture he spoke on lessons learned from Greek Medicine describing it as the taproots of Western civilisation.

> *What Socrates did for philosophy, Hippocrates did for Medicine and that remarkable document, the Hippocratic Oath, has been for 25 centuries the 'Credo', of the medical profession and it is in many universities still the formula by which men are admitted to practise as doctors. (Appendix 2).*

*Superfluity of lecturing causes ischial bursitis.*

His view on specialism in medicine may be applicable today. He said that there is a tendency to develop a narrow and pedantic spirit, and the man who year in and year out corrects errors in refraction, removes prostates or takes blood pressures without regard to the wider basis upon which his art rests will reach the somewhat limited attitude of mind of the old Scotch shoemaker whose answer to every question about the weightier matters of life was, "D'ye ken leather?"

The spring of 1911 saw Osler and his wife take a trip down the Nile and In May he received an invitation for the unveiling of Queen Victoria's Memorial in front of Buckingham Palace. The German Emperor and Empress also attended.

> *It was a glorious day all the men were in court dress or uniforms the royalties were numerous it was a brilliant sight. The king was gracious in manner and full of interest in everything.*

In June Princes and Princesses, envoys and ambassadors were arriving from around the world for the coronation of King George V, and the following morning there appeared in *The Times* a long list of Coronation Honours. This included Sir William Osler as a Baronet. He had previously shown his wife the letter, which came from 10 Downing Street marked 'confidential', and when they had an opportunity for a moment alone she asked, "What excuse are you going to give for declining it; you always have said you would?" He replied, "I think I'll have to accept. Canada will be so pleased, there's only one other Canadian Baronet."

*Let every student have full recognition for his work.*

When the news was out, he was inundated by messages from all over the world, and the President of the Royal College of Physicians, Sir Thomas Barlow, wrote:

> *You have all along been a peacemaker and binder together of different interests of medicine both at home and abroad and if for no other reason this distinction would have been fitting and suitable.*

Despite speaking in many places and being on many committees his university obligations continued unchanged. He took his regular Tuesday afternoon clinics at the Radcliffe Infirmary, the interesting cases continued to be written up to be published in medical journals at home or abroad, and he was kept very busy. On top of these duties was a further revision for the latest edition of his textbook.

On 10th February 1912 Lord Lister died suddenly from pneumonia in his 85th year and on 16th May a memorial service was held in Westminster Abbey. A grateful nation would have interred him there had not his express wish been to be buried at Hampstead beside his wife. Osler was at the service, which he described in a letter:

> *When the ear heard him then it blessed him; and when the eye saw him, it gave witness of him. He delivered the poor that cried; the fatherless and him that had none to help him. Kindness, meekness and comfort were in his tongue. His body is buried in peace, but his name liveth evermore. Only those who have lived in the pre-Listerian days can appreciate the revolution which has taken place in surgery.*

*More people are killed by over eating and drinking than by the sword.*

In April 1912, ten days were spent in Venice, Florence and Padua, all to the architectural awakening of Revere who had already been showing artistic skills in etching and photography. It was while they were there they heard the tragic news of the sinking of the *Titanic* on 14<sup>th</sup> April.

Although he was a member of various clubs where he could dine in the evenings, he preferred to use his home for entertaining, although he still dined regularly at Christ Church on Sunday evenings and attended monthly dinners of the Royal Society in London.

In the summer of 1912 they spent a happy holiday in the north of Scotland with Revere, home from Winchester College. They enjoyed trout fishing in the highlands and Osler spent one day accompanying the local doctor on his rounds in a district 40 by 25 miles. He returned via St Andrew's University, the only British University he had not visited.

In November the Bodleian underground book stack was formally opened and Osler gave the Bodleian Library a beautiful English mantle clock to replace Dr Rawlinson's which had become worn out after 160 years of service. It struck a soft unhurried chime appropriate for a library and Osler's hope was that it would last as long as its predecessor.

December saw him travelling daily to London each evening to attend Whitelaw Reid, the American Ambassador to Britain, who died peacefully on 15<sup>th</sup> December. Osler was said to be of more comfort to him than his British doctors.

In March 1913 he took a trip to Baltimore soon after attending the 300th anniversary of Sir Thomas Bodley's funeral service in Merton College chapel. On arriving in the United States he spoke on 'A Way of Life' to undergraduates at Yale, and related his recent journey across the Atlantic,

*Should your assistant make an important observation,*
*let him publish it. Through your students and*
*your disciples will come your greatest honour.*

standing on the bridge of the great liner ploughing the ocean at 25 knots, when all of a sudden a signal sounded and all over the ship the water tight compartments were closed. The safety of the passengers was their key concern, said the Captain, with the thoughts of the recent *Titanic* disaster fresh in the minds of everyone. Osler went on to say:

> *Now each of you is a much more marvellous organisation than that great liner and bound on a longer voyage. What I urge you to do is to control the machinery, to live with day tight compartments, as the most certain way to ensure safety on the voyage. Shut out the past, the dead yesterdays; shut off the future; the unborn tomorrows; then you are safe, safe for today. Don't see what lies dimly at a distance but do what lies clearly at hand: 'Do today's work today.'*

His lectures were given using lantern slides, and when one professor invited him to meet some of the faculty members he replied:

> *If you don't mind, I would prefer to meet undergraduates. I see dons every day at Oxford and not enough undergraduates from America.*

He sailed back to England at the end of May arriving in Oxford on the 23rd. This proved to be his last trip to America.

In 1912 the Prince of Wales (the future Edward VIII) had taken up residence at Magdalen College with directions that he should be put under the care of the Regius Professor of Medicine, and soon after Osler returned from the United

*The incessant concentration of thought upon one subject, however interesting, tethers a man's mind in a narrow field.*

States the Prince had an attack of influenza. It appears that Osler visited him on a number of occasions and after the Prince had left Oxford, a silver inkstand arrived as a present from the grateful patient.

He was in combative mood about the training of doctors. Replying to some letters in *The Times* about the suggestion that the doctor should be a practical man and not worry about science, he wrote

> *I should be sorry to have any student in whom I was interested come under the influence of a man who in these days could say that scientific education may be excellent as an idea but I doubt if it materially assists the average practitioner in the treatment of disease. Mr G represents a type, like the men who jeered at Harvey, scoffed a Pasteur and ridiculed Lister. The carpenters in surgery, and the pill mongers in medicine, without vision be on the bench or the counter, the tragedy is that the type persists today.*

Summer in Oxford was a peaceful time. Oxford was comparatively empty and every afternoon William and Revere would climb the fence and go down for a swim in the Cherwell at Parson's Pleasure. An area where men swam naked and ladies had to get out of the punts and walk around to avoid the sight. The facility closed in 1991 and the area now forms part of the University Parks.

Michaelmas term began and in due course the December examinations loomed for the medical students. As an examiner, Osler leant towards the indulgent side but never to the detriment of future patients. The Oxford examiners were

*Familiarise yourself with the work of others and never fail to give credit to the precursor.*

always invited to stay at 13 Norham Gardens during June and December, and Osler had been heard to remark after they had lunched, "There is just one thing to remember. Be lenient." His attitude met with strong opposition from those entrenched in the old ways but he objected to a system which kept men during their best years continually meeting tests on subjects they had long left behind.

Osler said there was no place like Oxford for a man who is past his most strenuous years and wants to combine occupation with enjoyment. He had them both in plenty. He had the ability to say the right thing to the youngest freshman and to the oldest don. He always appeared to be of a similar age to the person he was speaking to, not talking down to the one or talking up to the other. He was interested in other people and what made them tick. He was popular in both town and gown, the civic life of the community as well as in university and college circles. His spirit of personal friendliness and understanding did more to remove sources of friction and animosity amongst conflicting groups than countless formal gatherings.

*I would warn you against the trials of the day soon to come to some of you.... Engrossed late and soon in professional cares, you may... find, too late... that there is no place in your habit-stricken souls for those gentler influences that make life worth living.*

# CHAPTER 14: FIRST WORLD WAR

On 28th June 1914 a fanatical Serbian student assassinated Archduke Ferdinand and his wife in Sarajevo. Although this created the spark for the start of the First World War, it was initially overshadowed by the death of Joseph Chamberlain, one of the most important politicians of the time, and of whom Churchill said, "He made the weather". But the world was about to change. In July Churchill, who was then Minister of the Navy, was determined not to be caught napping and ordered a test mobilisation of the British fleet.

On 29th July Austria declared war on Serbia. Sir Edward Grey, who was Foreign Secretary at the time, had made a proposal for a peace conference which had been refused by Germany. On 31st July came Russian mobilisation, followed on 1st August by Germany's declaration of war on France and on 3rd August troops entered Belgium. Then the avalanche descended. By this time Osler was in the remote part of Scotland, while his wife and Revere had already sailed for the United States. On 4th August, the day after Germany violated the neutrality pact, England declared war, and in a few days the vanguard of the British Army was on French soil.

Getting back to Oxford, Osler found much to do. He was due to sail for America in early September but he wrote to Baltimore saying:

> It will be impossible for me to come over in these troubled times. We shall be here in the centre of the hospital work.

> *The plan is to utilise the university and college buildings. Already within the week the big examination schools have been converted into a hospital. Nearly 300 beds are ready and we could take patients in a few days.*

The number of beds grew rapidly. A few days later they were at 350 and then 480, and within a few weeks the Examination Schools had become a 1,000-bed hospital with an operating room, post-mortem room and chapel. Opposite, the Masonic Hall had 50 beds, and Magdalen School was turned into a hospital. Eighty beds were in the infirmary ground, 1,000 territorials were in Christ Church. Cambridge had also established 3,000 beds in a similar fashion, and military hospitals were being created all over the country. Osler was made a Colonel of the Oxfordshire regiments and ordered a uniform, as he could not go onto the wards without it.

He wrote to *The Times*:

> *In war the microbe kills more than the bullets. Malaria, cholera, typhus, typhoid, and dysentery have been the scourges of armies. From the first three, our soldiers are not likely to suffer but it will be very difficult to prevent outbreaks of dysentery or typhoid fever, of which in the South African war more men died than were killed in action. Against this we now possess an effective vaccine and I write to urge that anti typhoid vaccination should be made compulsory in the army.*

However, there was still great opposition from the anti-vivisectionists and the anti-vaccinationists to any compulsory legislation of this nature. So Osler appealed directly to the

*Acquire the art of detachment, the virtue of method, and the quality of thoroughness, but above all the grace of humility.*

enlisted men, pointing out that in South Africa there were 57,000 cases of typhoid fever. He left the decision to them.

In September 1914 the first German prisoners arrived in Oxford. They were described as fine looking fellows with trivial bullet wounds. Meanwhile Revere was 19 and had just started at Christ Church. Within the university regiments of students were organised under military discipline Revere entering the Training Corps in preparation for applying for a commission. Many European professors were fleeing to Oxford for safety, most absolutely penniless. Lady Osler was helping to settle them into lodgings in small houses, asking friends for donations to help. The refugees continued piling into England. Only one lamp was allowed on motorcars and in London rows of lights were put in Hyde Park to divert the attention of airships from Westminster Abbey and its treasures.

In December 1914 Grace Osler was busy with a group putting warm sleeves in 2,000 waistcoats and making pyjamas for the hospital. She wrote to a friend:

> *Every morning we read of friends being mown down. All the youth and glory of our country, many we have known, and here we have our only boy training in the park under our eyes, except that I can't look. Work is our only salvation and I keep at it from 9.00am to 11.00pm W.O.is busy and trying to be cheerful; hard work sometimes!*

Osler met Sir Frederick Treves, just back from the front, where he said that the organisation was much better than his South Africa experiences in the Boer War. Treves was the

*It is astonishing with how little reading a doctor can practice medicine, but it is not astonishing how badly he may do it.*

surgeon who operated on King Edward VII for an appendix abscess and delayed his coronation, and also who rescued 'The Elephant Man' from his life with a travelling showman and gave him a decent home for the rest of his life.

In another letter Osler wrote:

> *The news is suppressed but four of the crack regiments of this kingdom, regiments that contain the flower of the land and to which it was a distinction to belong, have been practically annihilated twice. Yet their ranks are filled up and you never hear a murmur. Presently it will be true that hardly a titled estate in England will go to its natural heir. The heir has been killed. Yet not a murmur: for England is threatened with invasion. They will all die first.*

He goes on:

> *Revere is a chip off the old block in his growing devotion to books but far more like his great-great-grandfather of the midnight ride in tastes and occupations. Skilful with tools and with the pencil. A self-taught etcher and even more skilful with his rod. His heart is not in drill or the war but he will do his duty when the time comes.'*

There can be no doubt that Osler wished to protect Revere as much as he legitimately could for his own sake more than his son's.

In 1915 Osler's name was being mentioned as a possible President of the Royal College of Physicians, but although he was honoured to be considered he felt that the man should be

*Patients should have rest, food, fresh air, and exercise – the quadrangle of health.*

resident in London. He went on to say that he had had enough of these things and was not especially ambitious in that direction. "To tell you the truth," he added, "I think the business would bore me to death."

He had now completed 10 years in Oxford.

> *Extraordinary happy years. Everyone is as kind and considerate as I could have wished, Grace has been happy and the boy has thrived. I had one attack of renal colic, the second in twelve years. The one thing I miss is active teaching and the close association with students and a large group of young doctors.*

On 7th May 1915 came news of the sinking of the *Lusitania* on which Lady Osler had travelled the previous year, causing the deaths of 1,198 passengers and crew, including 128 American citizens. This played a large part in drawing the United States into the war.

Revere had been posted to the Canadian McGill unit as the assistant quartermaster, and in September 1915 Osler visited the front line watching the wounded being brought back from the trenches. These included the son of the Speaker of the House of Commons who was shot through the chest. He thought the doctors and nurses knew their work and the officers' quarters were comfortable. Many of the men were sent back on the ambulance trains that same evening.

He describes the scene at the battlefront:

> *Stationary balloons, aeroplanes, soldiers, camps, billets in farms, brigades of artillery on the march – such a scene. In the field next to the chief medical officer's house, a big new*

*Anatomy brought life and liberty to the heart of healing, and for three centuries the great names in medicine were those of the great anatomists.*

*German aeroplane was brought down the day before our visit. We had hoped to go on the upper road to Hazebrouck but it had been shelled the day before and was impassable so we kept along the second line of trenches and in the evening saw many returning and going to them. Here for the first time we heard the boom of guns every minute. About three miles from Nieppe we saw the bombardment of aeroplanes by the German aircraft guns. The first one was 3-4,000 feet up at the edge of a light cloud and within five minutes 42 shells had exploded near it. We could see the bright flash and then a puff ball of black smoke, quite circular which then increased to about the size of the moon and gradually disappeared. Within half an hour we saw another much closer and 122 puff-balls could be counted near the clouds, many seemed so close but the aeroplane sailed about taking the usual daily observations…. Miles and miles of motor lorries line the roads waiting to go up in the evening. The peasants are hard at work getting in their crops, even between the lines of trenches…. Everywhere great squares of graves marked with the names of the men of the regiments.*

Revere came home on leave until 13th November. The family had a narrow escape on 11th when Grace was woken at 3:30am with the smell of smoke in the house and found the dining room on fire. It was 25 minutes before the Fire Brigade arrived. With wet towels over their mouths Revere and Osler managed to get out four shelves' worth of books and the Fire Brigade managed to save the rest.

During the war hundreds of telegrams and cables came to Osler from Canadians asking, "My son recorded seriously

*Full knowledge, which alone disperses the mists of the ignorance, can only be obtained by travel or by a thorough acquaintance with the literature of the different countries.*

wounded can you make enquiries?" All of which he did his best to answer.

The contrast between the front line and the peace of the Cotswolds could not have been starker, and back in England in May 1916 Osler took Grace with him for a consultation eight miles north of Oxford. They enjoyed the views cross the Cotswolds to Kingham and Chipping Norton and found a pleasant inn in which to have tea.

The hospitality at Norham Gardens continued, causing one visitor to write after her second visit:

> *You keep open house; you're always in evidence; you are always the same, welcoming them in and speeding the departure. You do the right thing always. You spend your life looking after other people, looking after the sick; your whole life is lived with others and the fact you get a certain amount of selfish pleasure out of being able to do it doesn't alter the least facts that you're wonderful.*

Revere decided his duty was in the fighting line and so left the McGill unit to take up a position in the Royal Field Artillery regiment of the British Army. His parents respected his decision but were deeply worried.

> *Our boy will be at the front sooner. We shall have to steal our hearts for the worst.*

October was a succession of gales and drenching rains. Revere reached France on 17th October 1916 and was promptly sent to the front with an ammunition column. During the rest of October and November he participated in the last stages of

*The physician needs a clear head and a kind heart.*

97

the Battle of the Somme, where 60,000 casualties had occurred on the first day.

Osler's brother Frank had just lost his only son and Revere was on the Somme in a dugout 100 yards from the German lines. December saw his 21st birthday, and Osler wrote, "Hard days on the heart indeed." In May 1917 Revere came back for his first leave in seven months. His father commented, "He went away a boy and returned a hardened man." They spent a happy ten days fishing and it was then back to Flanders where Revere was involved in the Messines Battle, storming the Messines Ridge. Osler wrote, "How badly you would feel if he would come back wounded but what a mercy it would be for him."

Several months later Revere was at Ypres with two million men massed within and at the back of Ypres salient. On 29th August Revere's battery received a direct hit. Major Bachelor, Revere (now a Lieutenant) and 18 men were bridging over a shell hole in preparation for the move at about 4.30 in the afternoon. They were so busy that they did not hear the sound of the first shell which dropped in the midst, wounding or killing eight of the twenty. Revere was mortally wounded and said, "This will take me home." He had multiple wounds to his chest, abdomen and thigh. A message was sent to Harvey Cushing who was at a nearby hospital and he drove by ambulance through the pouring rain. When he arrived he found Revere alive but in extreme shock. As Revere drifted in and out of consciousness, he was glad to see his father's old friend standing over him and smiled and said, "So glad you're here."

Revere was given a blood transfusion from one less seriously injured man from his own regiment, and late that

*If many drugs are used for a disease, all are insufficient.*

*Revere Osler*

night an operation was undertaken by other colleagues of his father. Cushing held his pulse but the wounds were too severe. He died before sunrise on 30<sup>th</sup> August 1917. Cushing cut a button from his tunic for his father and later described the scene:

> We buried him in the early morning. A soggy Flanders field beside a little oak grove on an overcast, windy, autumnal day. The long rows of wooden crosses – the new ditches half full of water being dug by Chinese coolies wearing tin helmets. The boy wrapped in an army blanket and covered by weather worn Union Jack. A strange scene. The great-great-grandson of Paul Revere under a British flag, and awaiting him a group of some six or eight American medical officers saddened with the thoughts of his father.

At 4.15pm the dreaded message came to 13 Norham Gardens: 'Revere dangerously wounded.' It was from Cushing, who did not have the heart to tell Osler that his son was dead. The War Office telephoned at nine o'clock at night to say that he had died. Osler wrote:

> We are heartbroken, but thankful to have the precious memory of his loving life.. We will take up our shattered lives and do the best we can.

Notes telegrams and cables poured in, mainly from American friends. In those days the English sorrowed in silence for one another. It was common for them merely to mention these things in an off-hand way. The Oslers longed

*Silence is a powerful weapon.*

to be alone in their grief but a Swiss physician failed to get the message and came to lunch. He only learned of Revere's death from the chauffeur on his way to the station.

Nancy Astor, an American-born English socialite and Member of Parliament, who at the age of 15 had been a patient of Osler's at Johns Hopkins, wrote after his death:

*I wish I could have seen you and told you of our beloved Sir William. It is almost impossible to write of him. I only saw him cross once with a young medical officer who said before a patient that his case was practically hopeless and that of course annoyed the chief. The great thing about him was he brought healing and health, life not death. Then after Revere died I shall never forget that day. We wondered if he could come back at once. We knew he would come back soon, but at once? Yes he was there in less than a week of receiving the news which I feel truly killed him. We all knew what was happening. We all knew his heart was broken. He went through the wards in the same gay old way but when he got to the house for lunch and alone with me he sobbed like a child – it was so hard for us who loved him.*

He said afterwards that, "I never saw a wounded man without thinking of Revere." The fact that Harvey Cushing and other colleagues of Osler's were at the casualty clearing station was a source of comfort to him. Christmas came with a full house and desolation in their heart. He had lost two stone since September. For his wife, of course, the grief was equal to his, although her time was spent in caring for him and doing her best to protect him.

*Respect your colleagues.*

In May 1918 Osler decided to bequeath 13 Norham Gardens to Christ Church as a permanent home for his successors. A memorial library in English literature was set up at Johns Hopkins in memory of Revere, where many of his books went to encourage the study of English literature of the Tudor and Stuart periods.

There was little jubilation for them both on 11th Nov 1918 as the armistice was signed and 1919 saw a slow return to post war life. At Encaenia in June many military personnel were present. Osler hosted an 'American invasion of No 13'. General Pershing, General Biddle and Mr Hoover arrived in preparation for the ceremony where they were, "brushed and polished by their aids", and as it was a cold morning Lady Osler lit a fire in the drawing room to which they all clung gratefully. Lunch at All Souls after the ceremony in the Sheldonian saw Lady Osler sitting between General Haig and Admiral Beatty. After lunch General Pershing dashed up to Blenheim for a visit and back to Wadham College for the University garden party.

*Remember how much you do not know.*
*Do not pour strange medicines into your patients.*

# CHAPTER 15: LAST DAYS

Osler was never the same after Revere's death, and Sir Charles Sherrington (neurophysiologist and subsequent Nobel laureate, who held the Waynflete Chair of Physiology) tells of an old servant in the laboratory who spoke about Osler:

> *No sir, I don't think Sir William will get well. You see sir, it's like this. You know how Sir William mostly on his way down to the Infirmary of a morning would drop in for a few moments to see you and the rest. Well, in the old days, coming in, and likewise going out, he had always a good word for me. You know his style sir, like giving a man a cheery digging in the ribs. But now these last months I've noticed him greeting you quite merry like; but in betweenwhiles his face has been grave as though he had something heavy on his mind and he is walked in and out without once noticing me. It's Mr Revere sir, and Sir William won't get better.*

The old servant had long seen what others had missed.

October saw Osler more seriously ill than usual with a fever and cough, and two colleagues from the Infirmary came to see him. He was still able to write postcards in November and insisted that the examiners should stay in December, but he was not well and had a persistent chest infection writing to one friend: "Abed, coughing, comfortable hopeful!"

However, the paroxysms of coughing became distressing to him and more so to his wife. On 5th December he had aspiration of his chest for pleurisy, empyema and a pulmonary abscess. On 10th December Sir Thomas Horder, physician to Edward VII, was called in and found "the infection strongly entrenched." Morphia was necessary to control the coughing. He had a further anaesthetic to drain his chest for a chest abscess. The end came at 4.30 on the afternoon of 29th December quietly and without pain after haemorrhage from the wound. The following day, in accordance with his wishes, a post mortem took place in 13 Norham Gardens by Dr Gibson, the attending physician. Osler had said he wished he could have been present, as he had a lifelong interest in the case! This confirmed the diagnosis of pleurisy, empyema and lung abscesses with death due to post surgical haemorrhage, and in those pre-antibiotic days the haemorrhage was probably a blessed relief from several further weeks of pain and discomfort.

At the time of his death Osler was probably the greatest figure in the medical world – the best known, the most influential, and the most beloved. No man was so capable of drawing together British and American medicine in the way that he did. He had no enemies. His reputation was founded partially on his scientific work but largely upon the inspiring and stimulating character of his clinical teaching. His legacy is nowhere better summed up than in his own words:

*I desire no other epitaph than the statement that I taught medical students in the wards, as I regard this as by far the most useful and important work I have been called upon to do.*

*The future is today.*

In the words of his biographer, Harvey Cushing,

*I doubt that a history of medicine records a man who had greater influence upon the students that came into his teaching, inspiring them with a remarkable devotion and affection. He was their example. His life embodied his precepts, and his students cherished his words, "Cultivate peace of mind and serenity, think not too much of tomorrow, but of the work of today, the work which is immediately before you."*

*He advanced the science of medicine yet individually he had a greater power. He became the friend of all he met. He knew the workings of the human heart metaphorically as well as physically. He joyed with the joys and sorrowed with the sorrows of the humblest of those who were proud to be his pupils. He stooped to lift them up to the place of his royal friendships, and the magic touch and tone of his generous personality helped many despondent in the rugged trials of life. He achieved many honours many dignities, but the proudest of all was his unwritten title, 'the young man's friend.'*

*Go out among your fellows, and learn of them.*

*William Osler, sketched by John Singer Sargent*

# APPENDIX 1
## PAUL REVERE'S RIDE

'Paul Revere's Ride' (1860) is a poem by the American poet Henry Wadsworth Longfellow that commemorates the actions of American patriot Paul Revere on April 18, 1775, although with significant inaccuracies. It was first published in the January 1861 issue of *The Atlantic Monthly*. It was later retitled 'The Landlord's Tale' in the collection *Tales of a Wayside Inn*.

Listen, my children, and you shall hear
Of the midnight ride of Paul Revere,
On the eighteenth of April, in Seventy-Five:
Hardly a man is now alive
Who remembers that famous day and year.
He said to his friend, — "If the British march
By land or sea from the town to-night,
Hang a lantern aloft in the belfry-arch
Of the North-Church-tower, as a signal-light, —
One if by land, and two if by sea;
And I on the opposite shore will be,
Ready to ride and spread the alarm
Through every Middlesex village and farm,
For the country-folk to be up and to arm."
Then he said good-night, and with muffled oar
Silently rowed to the Charlestown shore,
Just as the moon rose over the bay,
Where swinging wide at her moorings lay
The Somerset, British man-of-war:

A phantom ship, with each mast and spar
Across the moon, like a prison-bar,
And a huge, black hulk, that was magnified
By its own reflection in the tide.
Meanwhile, his friend, through alley and street
Wanders and watches with eager ears,
Till in the silence around him he hears
The muster of men at the barrack-door,
The sound of arms, and the tramp of feet,
And the measured tread of the grenadiers
Marching down to their boats on the shore.

Then he climbed to the tower of the church,
Up the wooden stairs, with stealthy tread,
To the belfry-chamber overhead,
And startled the pigeons from their perch
On the sombre rafters, that round him made
Masses and moving shapes of shade, —
Up the light ladder, slender and tall,
To the highest window in the wall,
Where he paused to listen and look down
A moment on the roofs of the town,
And the moonlight flowing over all.
Beneath, in the churchyard, lay the dead
In their night-encampment on the hill,
Wrapped in silence so deep and still,
That he could hear, like a sentinel's tread,
The watchful night-wind, as it went
Creeping along from tent to tent,
And seeming to whisper, "All is well!"
A moment only he feels the spell

Of the place and the hour, the secret dread
Of the lonely belfry and the dead;
For suddenly all his thoughts are bent
On a shadowy something far away,
Where the river widens to meet the bay, —
A line of black, that bends and floats
On the rising tide, like a bridge of boats.
Meanwhile, impatient to mount and ride,
Booted and spurred, with a heavy stride,
On the opposite shore walked Paul Revere
Now he patted his horse's side,
Now gazed on the landscape far and near,
Then impetuous stamped the earth,
And turned and tightened his saddle-girth;
But mostly he watched with eager search
The belfry-tower of the old North Church,
As it rose above the graves on the hill,
Lonely, and spectral, and sombre, and still.
And lo! as he looks, on the belfry's height,
A glimmer, and then a gleam of light!
He springs to the saddle, the bridle he turns,
But lingers and gazes, till full on his sight
A second lamp in the belfry burns!
A hurry of hoofs in a village-street,
A shape in the moonlight, a bulk in the dark,
And beneath from the pebbles, in passing, a spark
Struck out by a steed that flies fearless and fleet:
That was all! And yet, through the gloom and the light,
The fate of a nation was riding that night;
And the spark struck out by that steed, in his flight,
Kindled the land into flame with its heat.

*(the poem continues for another five verses)*

*Osler at work in Oxford*

# APPENDIX 2
## HIPPOCRATIC OATH

I swear by Apollo The Healer, by Asclepius, by Hygieia, by Panacea, and by all the Gods and Goddesses, making them my witnesses, that I will carry out, according to my ability and judgment, this oath and this indenture.

To hold my teacher in this art equal to my own parents; to make him partner in my livelihood; when he is in need of money to share mine with him; to consider his family as my own brothers, and to teach them this art, if they want to learn it, without fee or indenture; to impart precept, oral instruction, and all other instruction to my own sons, the sons of my teacher, and to indentured pupils who have taken the physician's oath, but to nobody else.

I will use treatment to help the sick according to my ability and judgment, but never with a view to injury and wrongdoing. Neither will I administer a poison to anybody when asked to do so, nor will I suggest such a course. Similarly I will not give to a woman a pessary to cause abortion. But I will keep pure and holy both my life and my art. I will not use the knife, not even, verily, on sufferers from stone, but I will give place to such as are craftsmen therein.

Into whatsoever houses I enter, I will enter to help the sick, and I will abstain from all intentional wrong-doing and harm, especially from abusing the bodies of man or woman, bond or free. And whatsoever I shall see or hear in the course of my profession, as well as outside my profession in my intercourse with men, if it be what should not be published abroad, I will never divulge, holding such things to be holy secrets.

Now if I carry out this oath, and break it not, may I gain for ever reputation among all men for my life and for my art; but if I transgress it and forswear myself, may the opposite befall me.

# FURTHER READING

*The Life of Sir William Osler,* Harvey Cushing 1926 Clarendon Press Oxford

*William Osler: A Life in Medicine,* Michael Bliss 1999 Oxford University Press

*Osler's a Way of Life and Other Addresses,* University Press Books, 2001

*Aequanimitas: William Osler,* McGraw-Hill Education, 2013

# END NOTE

1. The artist likes to be known as John Little. Photographic credit, Robert Derval.

# OTHER BOOKS BY DAVID CRANSTON

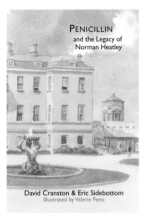

PENICILLIN and the
Legacy of Norman Heatley
*by David Cranston and Eric Sidebottom*
*with illustrations by Valerie Petts*

This is the real (and surprising) story behind the greatest medical achievement of the twentieth century.

I am amazed that it has taken so long to tell the story of Norman Heatley, the scientist whose talents made the development of penicillin, the world's first antibiotic, possible. He was truly 'the right man in the right place at the right time'. He deserves to be remembered, and this book will help to ensure that the true story of the birth of antibiotics is not forgotten.

The authors are to be congratulated on giving us this sensitive and sympathetic record of the life of 'the unsung hero of penicillin', Norman Heatley.

*Professor Matthew Freeman Sir William Dunn School of Pathology*

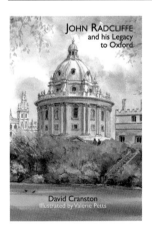

JOHN RADCLIFFE and his
Legacy to Oxford
*by David Cranston*
*with illustrations by Valerie Petts*

John Radcliffe's bequests have changed the face of historical Oxford, and their effects live on. David Cranston has performed a valuable service by showing how and why this came about.

*Professor Sir David Watson, Former Principal,*
*Green Templeton College*

# FIRST TIME MOM SURVIVAL GUIDE

*Don't Panic! We've Got Your Back. Be a Rockstar Mom & Prepare Every Step of The Most Exciting Journey of Your Life. Pregnancy, Labor, Childbirth and Newborn Baby Care*

# Table of Contents

# Introduction

Congratulations on purchasing this book.

The following chapters will discuss about every aspect of during and after the pregnancy: Expecting, Labor, Childbirth and Newborn. The information found in this book will best explore all you need to learn in order to experience a Healthy Pregnancy. It's your new mom's Survival Handbook.

Thanks again for choosing this audiobook! Every effort was made to ensure it is full of as much useful information as possible.

Please enjoy!

Every woman wants to fulfill her role of becoming a mother to her child. She dreams of carrying her unborn and giving birth to a healthy infant. There is something about first time pregnancy that makes it different and memorable. Nothing can compare to the excitement and anticipation of first time moms to conceive the bundle of her joy.

Along with the fervor of becoming a first time mom, you may feel a little confused, anxious, and fearful. The big responsibility of ensuring the good health and survival of the life inside your womb awaits you. To do so, you should prepare your body to give your unborn the healthy environment he/she needs to live.

It is easy to center your attention to the life inside your womb. You have to remember, though, that your unborn depends heavily on your own health and well-being. It is therefore essential that you have a body ready for pregnancy. Since this is your first time, you may need all the help you can get from your spouse, family, and friends.

You will also find valuable resources online. This pregnancy guide intends to help you how to take good care of yourself for your baby from conception to childbirth. Written for first time moms, it covers everything you need to know in preparing your body before, during, and after your pregnancy. This is the ultimate baby care guide for first time moms like you.

# Chapter 1: A Guide To First-Time Moms

So you want to be a good mom? Don't worry. You will be! You just need to know what to expect. This chapter is all about letting you know what you're in for –and while it's natural to be nervous about the whole thing, preparing for it will ensure that you and your baby will be healthy and happy.

First-time moms are in for a different kind of experience once a baby enters their life. It doesn't even start after delivery–it starts once you see those two pink lines confirming that you have a life in your womb. You'll experience a slew of emotions -- a mixture of excitement, happiness, fear, and many others. It's normal to be nervous. You'd even find yourself worrying a bit about pains during delivery. Aside from that, the imagination of a first-time mom usually goes into overdrive. You might find yourself thinking about the foreseeable future and worrying about whether you can give your baby a good life.

Emotions run high and you'll tend to be extra sensitive during pregnancy, thanks to hormones, which is why you really need to understand your needs and how your body works, and the changes that will occur–from the subtle to the not-so-subtle. If you do that, first-time pregnancy and parenting will be manageable.

The joys of pregnancy and parenthood are overwhelming, but pregnancies also come with a need for a great deal of work, patience, love, support, and understanding. Here are some of the challenges, reminders, and pieces of advice that you should consider so you will enjoy this new stage of your life.

What To Expect When You're Expecting

Conception, pregnancy, childbirth, and child rearing are no walk in the park. It's easy to say you want to have a baby, but once the baby is there, you discover how hard reality bites. Here are some expectations you need to be ready for:

The Pains of Childcare

Childcare will definitely burn your energy especially the first few years, and more so, the first few months. You should be ready for sleep interruptions during the night. You will get exhausted during the day may not have enough energy to look after the baby at night. Once you're back to work, you have that to worry about too. You might want to consider asking for a more flexible shift at work. If that isn't possible, hire a nanny who can look after your child. It is going to be worth it. Nothing compares to the feeling of waking up and staying late just staring at the little angel.

Set Your Priorities

Once you're confirmed that a baby is on the way, it's time to readjust your priorities. This is the first thing you have to remember–you should not try to be a superwoman. You don't have to make sure that your house is spotless, that you serve well-planned healthy meals all the time, maintain your relationships with all friends and work full-time all while taking care of your baby. You have to be realistic about what can be done without stretching yourself too thin. Find out what's more important to you and build your schedule around that. Perhaps, you don't have to keep the place spotless. Perhaps, eating outa few nights a week is okay. You don't even have to completely stick to a rigid schedule. Part of being a parent is thinking on your feet.

Establish a support system

You are going to be your child's anchor but it doesn't hurt to get support from other people, as well. Remember what they say about how it takes a village to raise a child. You don't need a literal village to help you out–you can just ask friends or family not exactly for help but for support. Ask someone over for dinner so you and your child can get some socialization with people other than each other. Also, contrary to popular belief, you can actually endear yourself to someone by asking for help–especially if it's something as easy as help with moving the couch. Even something as simple as calling your own parents to talk about how things are with your child is a good way to establish that support system.

Stay Healthy

Motherhood is going to take a lot of energy so staying fit is important. You should never forget to take care of yourself. That way, you can take care of your child and their needs. Motherhood is a 24/7 job, and you can't afford to get sick or fall to a serious condition because a tiny human being is now dependent on you. Still, you do need some time off to take care of your personal needs, which is why you'll need a readjustment of priorities and a decent support system.

It's challenging–but rewarding -- to be a first-time mom. There will be ups and downs, but if you are determined to take on the challenge, you'll find that it can be fun and exciting –even wondrous at times. Parenthood becomes even more meaningful once you start teaching your child the value of respect, love, and responsibility –and just how to be a good human being in general.

# Chapter 2: Things You Need to Consider When Preparing for Pregnancy

When you get pregnant, your body goes through major changes. You might think that all the changes hormones brought during puberty were enough to make you crazy but just wait until they get to work during your pregnancy! Hence, it's crucial that prepare physically and also mentally. The physical aspect is a given, of course. After all, you'll be nourishing a life inside you. But you see, pregnancy is bound to catapult you into something you may not be quite prepared for. Yes, you expect to get pregnant someday and you might have even been fervently wishing for it. Whatever the case may be, expectation can be quite different from reality; thus, the need to prepare yourself mentally.

You may need to consider your career. This consideration goes hand-in-hand with finances, which is also a crucial part of being a parent. You'd want to make sure that your baby's needs are taken care of. There are some important questions that you will need to ask yourself. How quickly do you intend to get back to work? How do you manage your career and a baby? Pregnancy doesn't come free. In fact, it is expensive. Can you afford to leave your job and risk going through mental stress while trying to think of how you can make ends meet and sustain your pregnancy? Bear in mind the medical bills, the cost of having the baby, baby needs and supplies, and even your own needs. That's why it's important to prepare yourself mentally for the pregnancy challenge.

The next thing you need to work on is preparing your body for pregnancy. As mentioned in the beginning, your body will undergo changes before, during, and after the pregnancy. Therefore, it's important to make sure that your body stays healthy through the entire process. The first thing you need to do is to optimize your weight. You want to enter your pregnancy in the pink of health, so you need to ensure that you are neither overweight nor underweight. Start maintaining a healthy diet. Consult your obstetrician for help on this regard or ask her if she can refer you to a nutritionist. If you were a smoker, now's the best time to quit.

Smoking can lead to low birth weight for your baby, premature labor, and a plethora of other health problems for both you and the baby, not to mention that it can make conceiving a baby difficult in the first place because of the fertility problems it brings. Avoid cigarettes and secondhand smoke.

You may also prepare your body for the pregnancy by taking supplements and prenatal vitamins. Vitamins rich in folic acid and iron are vital, and you would do well to take these in large quantities once pregnant.

# Chapter 3: Making it Through the Pregnancy

Keys to a Happy Healthy Pregnancy

It is ideal to start the lifestyle changes discussed in this chapter even before you become pregnant. But don't worry if you have not done it yet. You can always decide to adopt these changes as soon as you can.

Stay active.

Regular exercise will not only be good for you but for your growing baby, as well. It is important that you stick to a regular routine so you can ensure that your placenta grows big enough to supply oxygen and other nutrients to your baby. Regular exercise can also help keep your heart and your baby's heart in good condition. There have been many studies published to prove that women who remain active and exercise regularly have shorter, less painful deliveries.

Choose an activity that you find enjoyable. There is one basic principle you need to adhere to: always listen to your body. Don't do a particular exercise when it does not feel right. Don't attempt to beat your personal record or finish a marathon during your pregnancy.

Reduce toxins.

- Eat as much real and organic food as you can. Stay away from BPA and canned and processed foods.
- Stop using personal care products that include "parfum" or "fragrance" as ingredients. You can always choose products that have natural essential oils.

- Try making your own cleaning products or use natural ones such as castile soap, baking soda, essential oils and vinegar.

Eat whole foods.

It is ideal for you to eat a well-balanced diet that consists of sufficient amounts of vegetables, fruits, healthy fats and protein. Include a lot of leafy green vegetables in your diet because they are rich in vitamin B and folate, which reduces your baby's risks of neural tube defects.

Sufficient rest.

Your pregnant body needs sufficient sleep so that it will be able to revitalize itself from the higher demands of your growing baby. Even excessive worries and negative thoughts can drain you of physical energy. During the 1st trimester, you may have to sleep extra hours every day to allow your body to adjust to your pregnancy. Try taking a nap or a rest at any time in the day. Try to rest as much as you can.

Consider chiropractic care.

Getting chiropractic care during your entire pregnancy can remove interferences to your nervous system. It can relieve the tension in your back from carrying extra weight, as well as help in readjusting your posture. This can enhance the uterine function and overall development of your baby. It can also help balance your pelvis and remove unnecessary tension that is placed on your ligaments and muscles. Chiropractic care can also improve the positioning of your baby which can allow you to have better natural birth.

Educate yourself.

When you start announcing your pregnancy, a lot of people will start to give their unsolicited advice. They do not really mean harm but sometimes your family and friends can give you the wrong information. This is why it is very important that you perform your own research to see if any information, or any prescribed tests are truly necessary and if they have any side effects that you need to be aware of. Always keep in mind that you have the ultimate responsibility for your baby and every decision that is made is yours to make. Do not let anyone pressure you into something that you do not want to do, and do not feel guilty for your decisions.

Take dietary supplements.

Here are some of the dietary supplements you can consider taking during your pregnancy:

- Omega-3 which is important for the growth and development of your baby. It is also vital for the proper development of your baby's brain and nervous system. Make sure to ask your doctor which specific supplement is ideal for you to take.
- Vitamin D is important in reducing your risks of developing a lot of complications related to pregnancy, particularly gestational diabetes. Vitamin D is critical in the proper development of your baby's hormones, bones and muscles. It can also boost your own immune system while pregnant.
- Probiotics are important in helping your unborn baby obtain sufficient amounts of good bacteria that can help lower their risks of illnesses during the formative years.
- Folic acid allows the body to create new cells easier. During pregnancy, it can help increase the rate at which your baby develops. It can also help to ensure that your baby's lungs mature easier at the end of your pregnancy.
- DHA is important to your baby's brain development and it is important for establishing normal brain function. This is

a vitamin that is important during pregnancy, and essential for your baby after he is born.

- Iodine is a vitamin that is typically overlooked. Iodine is important for your baby's brain development during pregnancy and when you are breastfeeding. Since the type and amount of fish that you can eat is limited during this time, it is important that you seek it out elsewhere.

Prenatal Care

Prenatal care is extremely important to your unborn baby. This care allows your doctor to monitor what is going on with your baby while he is still in your tummy.

Prenatal care helps ensure that you and your baby remain as healthy as possible, and that any health conditions are taken care of in a timely manner. Your doctor will also be able to give you care advice that is customized to your individual needs, and what your baby needs.

Every woman, and her pregnancy is different. Even if you have been pregnant before, this pregnancy will be completely different. Therefore, you should treat this pregnancy as what it is, unique.

Most doctors recommend that you be seen in their office for prenatal care using the following schedule:

- Once a month for from the time you are one month pregnant until you are seven months pregnant.

- Two times per month from the time you are seven months pregnant until you are eight months pregnant.
- Every week from the time you are eight months pregnant, until you deliver.

At your prenatal visits, your doctor will do several things, including a physical exam and order lab work.

You can expect the following things to happen at some point in your pregnancy:

- Check your blood pressure at every visit.
- Determine how much weight you have gained.
- Measure your belly to see how much baby has grown.
- Check your baby's heart rate.
- Determine whether you have a family history of disorders that may affect your pregnancy.
- A physical exam, including a pelvic exam.
- Blood based laboratory tests.
- Answer any questions you may have about your changing body.

How You Can Prepare for Doctor Visits

Over the next eight months, you and your doctor will become very close. Your doctor will be your go to person for questions and concerns that you have during your pregnancy. They are a great resource, but only if you handle this relationship in the right manner. Here is some amazing advice to ensure that you get the most out of this relationship.

Select the Right Doctor

By choosing the right doctor, you are doing you and your baby a huge favor. When getting your needed medical care you should take the step to create a solid relationship as doctor and patient. You should also make sure that you feel the doctor you choose to see is compassionate and competent. Mary Jane Minkin, MD says "Trust is one of the most important factors in a good doctor-patient relationship."

Mary Jane Minkin is a clinical professor of gynecology and obstetrics at the School of Medicine at the Yale University. You and your doctor should be comfortable with each other. There should be no tension when he walks in the room or if you think he is mistreating you. If you think this is happening to you than you should try to find another midwife, doctor, or a new health care provider. You need to make sure that you find some one you click with and stay with them. Because there are so many legal issues there are a lot of doctors that are retiring from the field of obstetrics. This means that many of them have gone to being OB's.

Ask questions (within reason)

If this is your first time being pregnant than you no doubt have lots of questions. If you do than you most definitely should ask them. Just remember you only have so much time so try to ask a reasonable amount of questions. Make sure that you prioritize your most important questions so that you can ask a few at a time. This will make sure you get your most important questions answered first.

Write down your questions--and the answers

One of the most important things you can do when you have questions is to write them down in a notebook. This will make sure you don't forget what your questions were and you can take them with you to make sure you ask your doctor. You can also take your notebook with you so that when you ask your questions you can write down what the doctor has to say about it. This way you will have them with you all the time.

Tell your doctor at the start of your appointment that you have questions

Doctors have many preferences in when they like to ask you if you have any questions. Some will ask in the beginning or at the end. The ones that ask in the beginning of an appointment like to make sure that if it is something they need to check during the exam. You can also let them know in the beginning that there are things that you want to go over that might need checked during the exam.

Save late-night calls for emergencies

It is important to save questions that are not an emergency for your regular visits instead of taking up the doctors' time. Or you can call the office during business hours and ask questions.

Talk to the nurse

You can call your doctors office and talk to the nurse if you have any questions between appointments. There are some questions that nurses can answer immediately. This will keep you from having to wait on the doctor calling you back for an answer that the nurse could have given you. If the nurse can't answer your question they can arrange for the doctor to call you back.

Don't come spouting facts from the Internet

You can find some answers online. If you search the internet it helps to look for the websites that are legitimate medical sites. Also if you read something you should ask your doctor if what you read is true or not. You should not jump to conclusions from the internet and tell the doctor that what you read makes you think that you should have a C-section. Saying something like this can make your doctor become defensive and in turn making appointments intense.

Show that you're invested in your pregnancy

Here is one of the ways that you can help show your doctor that you really care and are going to invest time into your pregnancy. If you are a smoker and you choose to quit when you first find out that you are pregnant. This will allow the doctor to see that you truly care about the health of your baby and that your pregnancy goes more smoothly. This will make your life and the doctors life that much easier. The more effort you put into doing things right for your pregnancy the more the doctor will be willing to help you.

People will tell you throughout your pregnancy that you are glowing. It's true, you are. Pregnancy skin shines and you are beautiful. There are going to be times when you feel unbelievably womanly and graceful. You will feel like you could be Mother Earth herself. Truth time here. There are probably going to be more times that you feel like something the cat drug in. Pregnancy is hard. Truth time again. Morning sickness does not happen to everyone and some people barely get it. Some of you though are going to get it and get it bad. Holding down food, at least for the first few months, is going to be a memory for you.

Crackers do help. Ingesting a small handful of crackers before getting up out of bed in the morning can be a big help. It is important to eat small meals. If you start to feel like you are a little queasy or a little full then it is time to stop. You can always eat more later on! You are going to be thirsty when you are pregnant and it is very important for the sake of both you and the baby to stay well hydrated. However, when you have morning sickness do not guzzle water. If you drink too fast it is going to come back up. Just take small sips and you will have a much better chance to keep everything down.

Another good choice for morning sickness? Ginger! Some people drink ginger ale and some people take a ginger supplement. Another yummy way to do it is gingersnaps! They really do work but be careful not to scarf too many down at once. You don't want them coming back up!

For most pregnant women morning sickness does go away after the first three months. After that, if your sickness is gone, you may get very hungry! And yes, it is true, you will crave food. Cravings can be very hardcore! Don't be surprised if you burst into tears one day and cry your eyes out because the local mini mart is out of beef jerky or chocolate doughnuts. One month you may want nothing but steak lots of steak. Another month, meat may turn your stomach inside out and all you want to eat is cantaloupe. There is no rhyme or reason to it that's for sure!

Some foods you do need to avoid in pregnancy. You probably were not going to eat it anyway but no raw or undercooked meat. No rare steak for you girl! This does include fish so if you love sushi you will have to bid it farewell for a while. Oysters and clams are both a big no no. Eggs are ok but make sure to check that are pasteurized and cook them fully before eating. Truth time. No one likes to admit but a lot of people like raw cookie dough. In pregnancy though you are going to have to bake those cookies, raw cookie dough is definitely not allowed!

Your body and your mind is going to change. Having a child growing inside you is flat out amazing. Hearing the heartbeat for the first time is indescribable. You will feel emotions that you did not even know you were capable of having. A fierce protectiveness for the unborn child will seem to come out of nowhere. You will protect your stomach while out in public without even noticing you are doing it. One day you will feel a tiny flutter and wonder what if, this usually happens around month four, but the next flutter will be stronger and you will know without a doubt. It is your child in there moving and growing and kicking.

Your hair may look more lustrous and that is good because you are not allowed to dye it while you are pregnant. Your partner is most likely going to find you extremely sexy and believe it or not your sex drive is going to soar. If you were wondering, yes you can have sex while you are pregnant. You might even want to have a lot of it because the first few months after the baby is born are guaranteed to turn into a dry spell. If you experience any cramping or spotting after sex make sure to discuss this with your doctor. You are going to start to love your baby bump and continue to love it even as you grow. You will sing to your baby and people will say hello to the little one through your belly button. (Whether or not you want them to!) These changes are truly amazing!

Truth time. Not all the changes can be classified as amazing, in fact some or downright annoying and uncomfortable. Heartburn you should expect. Mothers that have never had heartburn will start to have it. Anything can cause it too, even sugar! It is unpleasant. Small meals and sleeping on pillows (so you aren't lying flat) can make a huge difference. Your boobs are going to get bigger, possibly a lot bigger! Yes, this can be nice. However, you will probably be surprised to see your nipples leaking. Months before your milk comes in, your colostrum can start to leak, this is normal! Colostrum is the thick creamy nourishment your baby will drink for the first few days of her life. So, if you see some leakage from your nipples, do not fear! If it worries you then calling your doctor is always a viable option.

In fact, do not forget that is why your doctor is there! Call their office anytime day or night when you are worried about something. It is their job to take care of you!

The more your baby grows the more your body stretches. Babies are so small you wouldn't think that your body would stretch too much, right? Wrong! The ligaments that run from your naval up to your ribs are going to hurt and at times they are going to hurt very badly. Getting off your feet whenever possible is always a smart decision. The longer you stand the more you are going to feel the stretch. There are products out there you can take advantage of. A belly belt is kind of like a girdle only it holds your baby up instead of your stomach in. The choice to use one of these is completely up to you.

Most likely you will find yourself unconsciously holding your baby up long before you deliver him. The tiny precious feet you are so looking forward to kissing or going to feel monstrous when they are in your ribs. Not only do all babies like to move and kick but they have some sort of sixth sense about kicking mommy directly in the ribs or jumping up and down on mama's bladder.

Speaking of bladders. Truth time again. There is a good chance you may pee your pants at some point. At the very least trickle. The last couple months of pregnancy the baby is growing rapidly towards full term size. Your internal organs fit inside you quite nicely before you got pregnant. Do they go anywhere when you are pregnant? Oh no! They just get squished! One day when you are nine months pregnant you are going to cough and see just how squished your bladder really is!

Sleep may be difficult, especially near the end. If you were a belly sleeper before you have some adjusting to do. Have you ever tried to sleep on your stomach with a beach ball underneath you? It just does not work. Anytime you can rest though take full advantage of it. Labor and delivery is coming and your body needs to be ready to handle it.

# Chapter 4: First Trimester: What They Don't Tell You

The first trimester of pregnancy is really an introduction period for your body and the new baby. Much is going on inside you and changes are happening to make room for the baby to grow. And get all of the nutrients it needs to mature into a full term fetus. The first trimester is the moment of conception up to the 12th week, or the 3rd month. For many women this is the most difficult trimester of them all. Your body is making a lot of adjustments.

The experience during first trimester varies for all women. You may not feel pregnant or then again you may feel very pregnant. Some women say that they have a full feeling inside of their stomachs from the very moment they conceive. Others even swear they know the exact moment that the baby was conceived. While there are no medical tests that can confirm a pregnancy this early, it is very much possible for a woman to have this type of experience.

It is hard to know for sure what you will experience or how intense your experience will be. Heartburn, morning sickness, being uncomfortable and nauseated -- these are all things that are commonly experienced by pregnant women during the first trimester.

What is the truth of the matter? Sometimes these experiences can be very difficult, and even if you have experienced them before pregnancy, these experiences are more intense during pregnancy. Heartburn is maximized 10 times over; your body is hot and you feel bloated. Even the smell of water makes you want to run to the bathroom to vomit. Morning sickness, even when you do not actually vomit, can cause pure misery. And, has anyone warned you about dry heaves? These are a few of the common experiences that occur during your first trimester.

Morning Sickness & More

Morning sickness should really have a new name because it is very misleading. It is sickness all right, but it does not discriminate and it causes trouble in more than just the morning. For some pregnant women morning sickness can be absolutely horrible, disrupting life in every single way. These women cannot stay out of the bathroom, and sometimes it is not that they are throwing up, but that they feel as if they want to 24 hours a day. It is not a pretty picture that we are painting here, and that is because there is nothing pretty about morning sickness. It can occur morning, noon and night, and sometimes it occurs during all three and never goes away. A package of saltines on hand to bite on when morning sickness strikes is the new-mom secret. A Sprite or ginger ale can also do the trick to ease your sickness. Do not think that you will only have mild nausea in the morning and it will all go away. This is one of the marks of pregnancy and most women will have it. And, chances are that it is going to be pretty severe for the first trimester. If you do not experience morning sickness, or if it is something that you experience only in mild form, then you are very lucky.

If you normally do not go to the bathroom very often, then get ready for that to change after pregnancy. The bathroom is your best friend during your pregnancy. Going there will be something that you have to do often! As soon as you wash your hands and get comfortable on the couch, you will have to go again. There's a lot of pressure with a baby sitting on your bladder, even if it does only weigh a half an ounce. The problem with frequent urination is that it doesn't go away until the pregnancy is over. In fact, the bigger baby gets, the worse the problem gets, too.

Heartburn, Acne & More

Heartburn is also something that you probably will experience during the first trimester. It is one of the most common side effects during pregnancy. Women who are pregnant with multiples report that the heartburn is even worse. However, most women with child will experience heartburn, and it really burns. It is a good idea to go ahead and get a bottle of Tums and expect to chew them like candy. You can drink water to help ease heartburn as well.

Even if you have been lucky enough to have never had a pimple before in your life, the hormonal changes with pregnancy may very well bring on an outbreak. For many women in their first trimester acne is a big concern. Many pregnant women fear using the products sold over the counter to get rid acne, scared that it will harm the baby. However, there are numerous home remedies for acne available that are perfectly safe for both mom and baby, while also being effective at eliminating acne breakouts. Some women experience no breakouts, some a few pimples and zits, and other women have full blown breakouts, and again, this is not something that anyone can determine ahead of time. If it does affect you, the key is to be prepared and ready to treat. If you do want to help keep your skin looking its very best, make sure that you wash the face twice per day, using a gentle soap or a mild cleanser. Follow up with a moisturizer to keep the skin soft. You can also talk to your doctor about acne treatments if you do not want to use those that are sold over the counter. Your doctor can give you many other tips and tricks to help combat acne as well.

You are going to be tired. Really tired. No matter how much you sleep it will never seem as if you have had enough. And, when you are awake you are probably not going to be jumping up and down and full of energy. Pregnancy takes a lot out of you. Make plans to settle down just a little bit, compared to your normal activities, that is. While you do not have to sit in the house and do nothing but protect your belly all day, you do need to make a few exceptions, avoid a few things and prepare for those days when staying in bed. You are not going to be getting a lot of sleep in nine months, and you are going to want it. So, go ahead and take advantage of it now, and sleep in when you can and put some of the normal activities to the side. The most important things that you can do right now is take care of your body and the new baby that is growing inside of you, and one of the things that you can do is get the extra sleep that you need.

An Emotional Roller Coaster

Aside from those kinds of changes, expect your emotions to be up and down. Many would suspect you were bipolar if they did not know you were pregnant. The smallest of things can cause an emotional meltdown -- and we do mean a meltdown. Uncontrollable crying isn't uncommon, and expect to be ultra-sensitive. You may cry over every single movie that you see, and something as crazy as getting a hamburger with a pickle on it can send you into frenzy. Your body is going through many changes. It isn't your fault; it is all of those hormones that your body is accumulating.

Mood changes are very common. One minute you are fine and the next you are not. It is just a part of pregnancy. This is first seen in the first trimester, but it is one of those things that continue throughout the entire pregnancy.

Here are a few other very important things that you need to know about pregnancy in the first trimester.

1. You will also worry about everything. What if you fall while walking down the street? What if something is wrong with the baby? Are you going to be a good mother? Will you produce enough breast milk? What are the best diapers? While seemingly irrational to the non-pregnant brain, prepare to worry about the smallest, sillier of things as if they were a major life decision. Just remember, this too

shall pass. It is not uncommon for pregnant women to worry about everything. It is a new experience and there is a lot that is going on inside of your body, after all.

2. During the first trimester you might also notice veins in your body that you have never noticed before. This is not uncommon and many women experience this. Whether in your arms or legs, veins seem to pop out of nowhere.

3. Noticing that your legs are a little hairier than they usually are, or that your hair is back the day after you shave? Again this is something that you should plan for and prepare for, because for most pregnant women it happens. Pregnancy is one of the healthiest times in the world, as long as you take care of yourself, and this means that hair (everywhere on the body) is growing rapidly. The hair on top of your head will also have this same effect. If you have thin hair, ordinarily expect to get a totally new mane that you will absolute love.

Your Doctor Visits

There is little change that comes during the first trimester physically, and chances are that most people will not even realize that you are pregnant. Although they say that you cannot feel baby move around until many weeks into the pregnancy, it is very much possible to feel butterflies in the stomach, which is the baby. This is just something that you know when you feel it. It is certainly a feeling like nothing else in this world.

The doctor will see you once a month during the first trimester, and sometime during the 8th week he will listen for a heartbeat. This is an amazing sound to hear. Some doctors will record it for you if you would like, and this is definitely an amazing memory to have to hold. Your doctor will also give you a due date, a date of conception and a ton of information to take home with you and read, including pregnancy magazines.

Most moms would tell you to read these books and learn as much as you can, and you should. But, at the same time, remember that you need to give yourself leeway and rarely does a pregnancy happen just as they predict in those magazines. Every woman will have her own unique experience and this is all a part of the enjoyment of being pregnant. Learn from the books and magazines and do all that you can to abide by the rules and the tips that they offer. But at the same time, do not make the mistake of thinking that everything is going to happen just like it says in those books.

And, another tip, do not throw all of those advertisements away. You are still new to being pregnant, and you are still unaware of just what it means to be a new mom. But, the pregnancy companies out there do and they are ready to help you out. Baby will drink a massive amount of formula, and at a cost of about $30 a can, this can get expensive quickly. Add to that the cost of diapers and you have a very expensive new life forming inside of you. It is all worth it, but you might as well take advantage of all of the help that you can get. Many of those advertisements that you see in magazines are for baby clubs. It is a good idea to go ahead and join them now. You will get plenty of full size products in the mail and lots of extra goodies, too. This can include diaper bags, bottles, wipes, formula, birth announcements, photos and more. You never know what kind of offers that you will find inside, but join all of the clubs that you can!

# Chapter 5: What To Expect During The Second Trimester

Week 13

This is the onset of the second trimester, and your baby is now at 7.5cm in length and 25 grams in weight, which is actually the size of a peach. The skeletal part of your baby's body begins to develop starting with the collar (clavicle) and thigh (femur) bones. Also, your baby starts to turn its head, swallow and hiccup. The baby can also kick their legs. The baby's stomach and vocal cord start to develop at the 13th week. In addition, your baby starts to take his first breath. The blood from the umbilical cord supplies the oxygen, and with a closer look it will seem as though your baby is breathing under water.

For you, you should be back to your normal self with minimal episodes of morning sickness, and the good news is that your chances of having a miscarriage is now a low probability. Also, you should notice a little more expansion of your waistline and bust.

Week 14

Your baby is becoming bigger and stronger at this stage. The arms are fully grown in proportion to the rest of the body while the legs are still undergoing growth. The baby's length is 8cm (about half a banana) while the current weight should be around 42 grams. The baby has hair and the eyebrows are formed before the end of this week. One surprising development process that occurs at this stage is the development of your baby's fingerprints. The baby will also start sucking their thumb. Also, your baby will start making use of their facial muscles to make expressions like squinting, frowning and grimacing.

You may suffer occasional forgetfulness as a result of the pregnancy hormones in your body. Also, nose bleeding is to be expected at this stage and you will experience a huge craving for food.

Week 15

Remember that I mentioned earlier that the baby's head was a third of its entire body. The good news is that by this fifteenth week, your baby's head must have grown into proportion with the rest of the body. The baby is 11.5cm (about the size of an orange) long, and his ears are fully developed at this stage to hear sounds. The baby will also grow some fine downy hair referred to as lanugo meant to keep the baby warm until they are able to develop a layer of subcutaneous fat to keep them warm after birth. The baby's sucking, swallowing and gasping skills have also advanced and will probably have developed their taste buds. The baby can also hear your voice by now so you should try to sing to them or talk to them often.

Although your baby's eyelids should still be closed at the moment, he can recognize lights. For instance, if you put a flashlight directly on your belly, you will feel some movements; that is your baby moving away from the light.

You will notice a dark line from your navel and down your abdomen and your baby bump starts getting noticeable.

Week 16

Your baby is probably the size of an avocado. At this stage, your baby's joints and limbs should be fully developed. Their backbone is also a lot stronger and they have probably mastered the art of sucking the thumb. Also, your baby's nervous system starts to connect with other muscles that will help your baby's movements. I talked about your baby developing skin much earlier. The skin at this stage is so transparent that you can clearly see the tiny veins underneath the skin. Their facial muscles are also a lot more developed so their expressions are a lot more visible although the baby doesn't yet know how to control them. The baby will also develop the ability to grab and play with the umbilical cord.

Your libido increases considerably. You will find yourself feeling the urge to have sex more often than usual. You can have as much sex as you want at this period without harming your baby. All you need to do is to find a comfortable sex position since your bump might get in the way.

Week 17

Your baby weighs around 150g in this week, and his or her facial features are fully developed. You may start feeling some firm movements in your womb. Your baby's brain begins to regulate the heartbeat to 140 to 150 beats per minute, which is still twice your own heartbeat. Meanwhile, your baby's fingerprints become more pronounced at this stage.

You will start feeling more energetic and less tired than you have in the past weeks. Now is the time to make use of that energy. Get the baby's room ready, take a workout class for pregnant mothers or join a walking group. Get out there and put that energy to good use! Getting more physically active now will help greatly later on, trust me!

Week 18

Your baby at this stage has grown to 14cm, and weighs almost 200g. The eggs start developing (in a female child), while the nerves begin to build up a protective covering referred to as myelin to enable the nervous system to develop and function properly upon birth. The baby at this period has also been engaged in lots of movements including kicking, tumbling and rolling. Their grip is also developed. The baby is also able to hold their umbilical cord firmly when playing.

Meanwhile, you tend to add more weight as the days go by. This is a combination of your weight, your baby's weight, the amniotic fluid, and the placenta.

Week 19

Your baby weighs about 240g and is about 14cm long at this stage. The baby's weight is more than that of the placenta now. Your baby's legs have grown into proportion with the rest of his body while the cartilage continues to harden. The baby's skin becomes less translucent and the skin pigments, which will determine the color of your baby's skin, will start to form. The baby will also start developing the Vernix Caseosa (this is the waxy or cheese-like white substance that coats your baby's skin when he or she is born) on its body to protect its body from the side effects of his contact with amniotic acid. The baby will also start developing some hair on its scalp, although the hair at this stage will be white and pigment free since the baby's hair color is yet to be determined. The baby can hear you well at this time.

You will notice a considerable increase in your bump size. Also heartburn and indigestion will be some of the symptoms that may occur during this period.

Week 20

Your baby is entering his fifth month this week. He or she will grow stronger and bigger to 16.5 cm length size; about the size of a banana but growing pretty fast. Also, at this stage, the part of the brain that controls the senses will start developing to help your baby to taste, see, touch and smell.

Your baby will also start producing something referred to as Meconium, within their bowel. Meconium refers to a harmless mixture of the amniotic fluid, which the baby has swallowed already, coupled with dead skin cells and digestive secretions. This mixture forms the baby's first bowel movement just after birth.

Your back may start aching as your bump continues to get bigger. Also, you may experience pain in your pelvis at this stage in your pregnancy as well.

Week 21

This week, your baby has increased in length to make him or her about 27cm long and weighing about 360g. Although your baby continues to add weight, it still lacks fats in its body. However, they will start adding on some fats that will ultimately give them the chubby 'baby' look when you first see them. The eyebrows have also developed and the eyelids can actually blink at this time.

One good point at this stage is that your baby's taste buds are fully developed to enable them to taste different flavors from the food you eat as they swallow the amniotic fluid. Also, the vernix caseosa is fully developed right now.

You should be making frequent visits to the antenatal ward by now. Antenatal classes help you (and your partner) prepare for labor, birth and early parenthood. You might also be interested in breastfeeding workshops as well.

Week 22

The baby is now about the size of a papaya, about 27cm from head to toe and still growing fast. The body will also keep growing its placenta to provide nourishment for the baby.

The baby at this stage gets his nourishment from the placenta instead of the yolk sac, and his or her gums and tooth bud are in place now. Although your baby's eyes are fully developed, the eyes have no color because of the absence of the pigment in their iris. Your baby has now mapped a sleeping and waking up time for themselves and the pancreas is intact now.

Your major problem at this stage will be your swollen feet and ankles as your baby belly becomes bigger.

Week 23

Your baby looks more like a newborn baby but just smaller. It is now 30cm long and weighs 500g, and its body at this stage has started producing fats, so it will start bulking up from this week. When the baby is very active, you should be able to see him or her moving under your skin. The skin is still translucent such that you can see the bones and organs through the skin. At this age, the baby won't jump as much when exposed to loud noises. You can start playing classical music to sooth them.

You will continue to notice a considerable weight gain in your baby, which is also manifested in your own weight gain.

Week 24

Your baby is 1 foot long, and weighs 600g. Medically, it has been proven that a baby born at this stage (that is prematurely) has a high survival rate. Your baby can detect the sound of your heartbeat and your voice at this stage while his or her eyebrows and hair are fully developed now. Additionally, the baby's lungs have grown such that it can now breathe in actual air rather than fluids (thanks to the production of surfactant. If the baby doesn't produce this substance, it will have some breathing problems) and their face has nicely developed eyebrows, eyelashes and hair, which is still white (lacking pigmentation).

You may experience bleeding in your gums around this time, which is one dental problem that is synonymous with pregnancy.

Week 25

The baby at this time is growing fast. He or she gets to the size of 13 ½ inches long and with a weight of about 1 ½ pounds. The baby also starts plumping up thanks to the buildup of fat deposits under the skin to make them look more like normal. The baby will probably be hyperactive at this period (with such activities like somersaults, and wriggling). They will also be responsive to certain sounds so singing to them wouldn't be a bad idea.

Week 26

Your baby has grown to 2lbs and 35.5cm long, and the eyes are finally open. There is an increase in your baby's brain activity during this period and the testicles (if it is a boy) are descending to his scrotum (this takes 2-3 months to complete). You will probably start experiencing some more contractions, which are similar to menstrual cramps coupled with pain as the developing fetus stretches the uterus. The baby's circulatory system is well developed while the umbilical cord keeps on thickening as it gets stronger to support the supply of various nutrients to the baby.

Week 27

Your baby's weight is at 875g now and his eyesight has developed well enough to differentiate between night and day, but that doesn't mean that your baby will keep to the rule of sleeping in the night. Also, your baby's brain is in the final stage of development now. The baby also hiccups often and will probably do that more often when you eat spicy foods.

Your appetite is likely to increase and you will have cravings for food you don't typically eat as part of your normal diet. Like the famous pickles and ice cream combo.

**Tips To Survive The Second Trimester**

Backache

There is extra pressure on your back from carrying your baby. You can ease it off a bit by always using a chair with back support, sleep on your side with a pillow in between your legs and avoid picking heavy items off the ground.

Nosebleeds

The mucous membrane in your nose is swollen because of the hormonal changes taking place in your body, which may lead to constant nosebleeds for you. You need to keep your head up and apply gentle pressure to your nose to stop the bleeding.

Appearance Of Varicose Veins

They appear as a result of an increase in circulation of blood in your body to send blood to the growing fetus. The veins will disappear with time after birth.

Weight Gain

After your morning sickness subsides, your appetite returns in full force. You are likely to gain 1 to 3 pounds every week during this time. You have to work on practicing portion control for whatever you eat.

Nutrition

Vital organs of the body are beginning to develop. As such, you have to continue with foods high in protein and vegetables. Eat more of fiber-filled food to keep you full.

Exercise

With the stop in morning sickness and the regaining of your strength, you can start mild workout regimes, yoga, and meditation to keep fit.

Braxton Hick's Contraction

This is also known as fake contraction, and occurs towards and during the later part of the third trimester. The Braxton hick is a warm up exercise to prepare your uterus for labor. There is nothing much you can do about the fake labor but if it becomes so intense, then you may need to visit the hospital. At this time, you can probably sense some metallic taste in your mouth due to toxins accumulation from the lymphatic system. Don't worry; it will improve with time.

Colostrum leakage

Besides having tender breasts, you will probably start producing colostrum (a liquid from the breasts, which is often clear or creamy yellow with the consistency of syrup) from the 14th to the 16th week. If you notice some blood here, this is probably due to the rapid growth of blood vessels growing in the ductal system as your body preps for breastfeeding. Use breast pads inside your bra to deal with this.

Skin changes

Your skin, hair, and nails might start having changes like pigmentation, stretch marks, red spider veins, hormonal rashes, dry and oily skin, skin tags etc. Worry not because this is completely normal.

Swelling and fluid retention

This is referred to as edema (this starts at around 20 weeks into the pregnancy). You may also notice swellings on your hands, legs, and feet; these often become worse when it is hot. Varicose veins are usually linked to causing swelling. You should try to get your blood pressure tested if your swelling doesn't go away after week 20.

Gestational hypertension

This might happen when you are around 20 weeks pregnant. And if you have gestational hypertension coupled with high protein levels in your urine, you might be suffering from preeclampsia, which is usually characterized with kidney problems, visual changes and headaches.

Note: Having gestational hypertension is likely to make you increase your risk of stillbirth, intrauterine growth restriction, preterm birth, and placental abruption. Get your weight under control because this is closely linked to gestational hypertension.

Gestational diabetes

Ensure to have your blood sugar tested just to help you determine whether you might be having gestational diabetes since suffering from this could put you and the baby at risk. Weight and your diet are key determinants of this. Therefore, making some necessary changes to your diet could minimize your chances of developing such problems.

You will also need to deal with rapid weight gain, weird dreams, itchy breasts, sleeping problems, increased libido and energy, leg cramps, itchy bumps, heartburn, backache and others. These shouldn't be any problem, as they will pass with time.

# Chapter 6: What To Expect In Your Third Trimester

The third trimester is the final trimester of your actual pregnancy! While many believe that pregnancy will continue into a fourth trimester, or your postpartum period, your physical pregnancy will be done by the end of this trimester! That is, you will be giving birth to your baby! This final trimester brings a whole new myriad of symptoms, if you didn't already guess that, but at the same time after all of this practice, you are probably more than ready to manage them!

During the third trimester, you are going to want to be extra cautious of your body, because this is when labor will happen! For some women, labor happens on or after their due date, but for others they can go into early labor. It is important that you stay in tune with your body so you can alert your doctor if any major changes occur. In this chapter, you will learn what normal symptoms are, and what you should look out for! As well, you will learn more about what to expect with your doctors' visits.

SYMPTOMS

The symptoms you will experience in the third trimester are different, but not terribly different, from those you have already experienced. For the most part, they will simply be exaggerated versions of the symptoms you've already been experiencing. However, there are a few additional ones you might experience. You can learn all about it below!

LEG PAINS

This trimester, you are going to continue to experience the leg pains you have already likely been experiencing throughout the second trimester. The larger you get, the more pressure it puts on your legs and it can become very painful. Luckily, these will go away once your baby is born! In the meantime, you should do your best to stay off of your feet for long periods of time. You can also drink coconut milk or eat bananas, which are both rich in potassium, a nutrient that can significantly help reduce leg cramping.

NECK AND SHOULDER PAIN

Your growing belly is putting a lot of forward pressure on your back, which can also affect your neck and shoulders. You may notice your neck and shoulders are feeling just as bad as your lower back feels. This is completely normal. The best thing you can do is take a warm bath (but not hot!), get gentle massages, and relax a lot. If you find that it is affecting your sleep, try using body pillows and other pillows to help you support your back, legs, and belly.

HUNGRY, BUT NOT

A symptom many women report feeling that is extremely uncomfortable is the feeling that they are incredibly hungry, but are not able to eat. This is because your body needs more nutrition in order to support the growing baby. However, because your baby is getting so big, your stomach is running out of room! That means you don't have to eat as much to feel incredibly full. The best way to combat this symptom is to eat high-protein and nutrient rich mini-meals several times throughout the day. This will help keep you full and give your body all of the nutrients it needs without feeling excessively full.

LACK OF BLADDER CONTROL

Many people experience lack of bladder control when they are in their late pregnancy stages. The best thing to do is stay near a washroom, and relieve your bladder regularly. You may also wish to wear a pad if you will be going out, as they help to keep you from accidentally peeing your pants. As well, you may wish to lean forward when you are peeing to help get all of the urine out of your bladder, as the pressure of your baby may prevent you from eliminating your bladder completely.

CONSTIPATION

While your urine may be hard to stop, your bowels may slow down all on their own. This is caused, again, by all of the pressures and hormones going on in your body. You can combat this symptom through eating dates, prunes, and other fiber-rich foods that can help keep things flowing. As well, make sure you're staying hydrated, as that is important for you and your body, and it will help keep things moving.

DOCTOR VISITS AND MEDICAL TESTS

Your third trimester is going to be the most intensive one you will experience in regards to doctors' appointments. Towards the end of your third trimester, you are going to have your doctor visits increase to weekly visits. The exact time this will happen will depend on your doctor, the healthiness of your pregnancy, and whether or not you have been showing any signs of labor.

The doctors' appointments in this trimester will continue to include all of the same things as previous ones did: they will weigh you, measure your abdomen, check your blood pressure and pulse, and take a urine sample to check for protein in the urine. Towards the end of the trimester, you will likely also get pelvic exams to see if your cervix is dilating at all. At the end of each appointment, you will be informed of what to look for in the coming days.

You actually won't experience any medical examinations this trimester, unless you are carrying an at-risk pregnancy. If you have high or low blood pressure, gestational diabetes, or any other pregnancy ailment, your doctor may require you to get an ultrasound or blood test taken to monitor your pregnancy a little more closely. Otherwise, you will not experience any further medical tests!

# Chapter 7: Pregnancy Symptoms You Should Not Ignore

For many women, the third trimester goes all the way through effortlessly. For others, particularly those who are carrying at-risk pregnancies, you might run into a few complications. While your doctor has likely discussed this with you, particularly if you are known to be a high risk pregnancy, it can still be good to have this knowledge on hand. The following symptoms are things you should never avoid during your pregnancy. If any of these occur, you should call your doctor immediately or head to the maternity ward at your hospital.

EXCESSIVE PAIN ANYWHERE IN YOUR BELLY

Experiencing aches and pains is completely normal during pregnancy, especially in the third trimester. As your baby grows more and more, he or she will be running out of room and you may experience pain due to your baby's movement. However, if you are experiencing severe pain that is not related to the baby moving around, regardless of where it is in your stomach, you should call your doctor right away. You should be sure to monitor it especially if this pain persists or won't go away no matter what you do.

A HIGH FEVER WITH NO SYMPTOMS

If you have an extremely high fever but aren't experiencing symptoms of the flu, you should contact your doctor right away. This is not a common symptom late in pregnancy, and could indicate that you are presently fighting an infection. Your doctor will be able to help you confirm an accurate diagnosis and help reduce your fever depending on what he or she discovers.

## EXCESSIVE VISUAL DISTURBANCES

While a slight change in vision is normal during pregnancy, excessive visual disturbances are not. If you are experiencing double vision, blurred vision, dimming or flashing spots, or other lights that are lasting for more than two hours or that are making you feel unwell, you should call your doctor right away. These symptoms are not normal and should be addressed immediately.

## EXTREME SWELLING IN HANDS AND FEET

Swelling due to increased blood volume and fluid retention is normal, but extreme or excessive swelling in your hands and feet are not. If these symptoms appear suddenly or are accompanied by a headache or problems with your vision, you should contact your doctor.

## SEVERE HEADACHE THAT WON'T GO AWAY

If you are experiencing a sudden and bad headache that won't go away after two to three hours, you should contact your doctor. If you are experiencing a headache alongside excessive swelling or visual disturbances, you should call your doctor right away and get seen as soon as possible.

## ANY AMOUNT OF VAGINAL BLEEDING

When labor is about to start, you may experience something called a bloody show. However, if you experience bleeding that is heavy, light, dark, or otherwise abnormal, you should contact your doctor. In the earlier stages of pregnancy, light spotting is usually just implantation bleeding. However, any time after implantation, any amount of blood may be a concern. You should also look out for other symptoms, such as abdominal pain or back pain, which can be a potential sign of miscarriage.

## FLUIDS LEAKING FROM YOUR VAGINA

It is really common for you to experience an increase in cervical discharge, as your body is working harder to keep potential bacteria build up out of your body to prevent infections. However, if you notice a watery fluid leaking from your vagina before 37 weeks, you will need to call your doctor right away. They will likely want to admit you to the hospital to check on your membranes and make sure they haven't ruptured. If they have, they will need to treat you to help prevent infection and prepare you and your baby for a potential premature labor and birth.

## A SUDDEN AND DRAMATIC INCREASE IN THIRST, WITH REDUCED URINATION

Pregnant women are at risk for dehydration, so it is important that you are drinking a lot of water throughout your entire pregnancy. However, if you notice that you are suddenly starting to feel extremely thirsty, and you aren't urinating as often, you will want to talk to your doctor. This can be a symptom of dehydration, or it can be a symptom of gestational diabetes. Your doctor is the only person who can determine the exact cause, so you will need to speak with them to get assistance.

## URINARY TRACT INFECTION SYMPTOMS

Urinary tract infections can be particularly dangerous during pregnancy, so you will want to discuss any UTI symptoms you may experience with your doctor. They will treat you and help ensure that the infection does not affect your uterus or your growing baby.

## SEVERE OR EXCESSIVE VOMITING

Vomiting has the ability to cause dehydration and weakness in anyone, but especially a pregnant mother. While vomiting itself doesn't necessarily indicate anything is wrong, and it won't hurt your baby, you should make sure you keep your doctor in the loop about this. This will help them monitor you and ensure you aren't becoming severely dehydrated. If you are vomiting too much, you may need to be admitted to the hospital to receive fluids in order to keep you hydrated.

If you are later in your pregnancy and start suddenly vomiting an excessive amount, especially with a pain just below the ribs, you should call your doctor right away. This can be a symptom of a few different complications, all of which will need to be treated by a doctor.

FAINTING OR DIZZINESS

If you haven't eaten enough during the day, you may experience fainting or dizziness. However, it can also be caused by low blood pressure. It is important that you contact your doctor about this symptom if it is persistent, or if you faint at all. They will want to make sure that you are well, and work with you to prevent it from happening again.

SLOWED DOWN FETAL MOVEMENTS

Most often, your doctor will ask you to monitor fetal movements, to ensure your baby is moving regularly. If at any time you realize you have not felt your baby move in a while, or you perform a kick count and your baby is not as active as normal, you will want to contact your doctor. In most cases, this simply means the baby is resting. However, in some extreme cases, this can be a problem that needs to be addressed immediately.

OVERALL ITCHING, SEVERE ITCHINESS

When you are pregnant, you are likely to experience itchiness in your belly and back area as your skin stretches and grows to accommodate for the growing baby. However, if you are noticing that your entire body is extremely itchy, particularly in your palms and the soles of your feet, you should call your doctor.

SYMPTOMS OF JAUNDICE

Any symptoms of jaundice need to be immediately addressed by your doctor. This can include: yellowed skin or eyes, dark urine, and pale stools. If you have any of these symptoms, you need to talk to your doctor immediately as they will want to have you admitted to the hospital for treatment. Jaundice is caused by an underactive or infected liver, and this needs to be addressed immediately.

IF YOU FALL OR EXPERIENCE A TRAUMA TO YOUR BELLY

If at any time in your pregnancy you fall or experience some kind of trauma to your belly, such as it being hit by something, you need to visit your doctor. While your belly will be fairly resilient, it is still important that you doctor ensures nothing has impacted the baby in a bad way. You should call your doctor immediately after a fall or blow to your belly to get help.

IF SOMETHING JUST "FEELS" EXTREMELY WRONG

Some women do not have an exact symptom of anything wrong, they simply feel extremely wrong. If you think something is not right with your body, baby, or pregnancy overall, you should talk to your doctor. They will look over your vital signs and ensure everything is wrong. While in many instances this can arise from anxiety, in some cases this feeling can indicate something is wrong, despite no symptoms really being present. Always trust your intuition!

More Pregnancy Secrets No One Tells You

We hope that you have gained a lot of information that you did not already know about your pregnancy and are now preparing adequately. Pregnancy is an amazing journey, and, when you know everything that is probably going to happen, it can be an even easier journey for you to make. However, we are still not done and there are a lot of other pregnancy secrets that no one ever seems to tell you but you still must know. If you want to know the rest of those secrets, keep reading.

Touchy Feely Kind of World

It is up to you as to how you will react, but go ahead and start planning it now: People are going to touch your belly. Yes, you can expect all of your family and your friends to do it, and that is annoying enough. (If you don't think so now, just wait. You soon will understand.) But what is really, really bone chilling is that it is not just family and friends who will want to touch the baby belly. The ladies in the supermarket will simply need to put their hands on the belly. Every kid that you encounter when you are shopping is going to touch your belly, or at least ask if they can. Heck, even the mailman might see the belly and feel the desire to touch it. People come out of nowhere to touch a pregnant belly and they could care less to whom that belly is attached. It is just something about that pregnancy belly that people find irresistible. You can politely ask people not to do it, but if you are like most moms you will just suck it up and go with it. It's kind of nice to be fussed about after all.

People Love to Talk

These is really no way to know what will come out of the mouths of some people upon learning that you are pregnant, so do not let anything that you hear surprise you. Sometimes, it is information that is very much unwanted, but it is all given to you with the best of intentions, in most cases. Be prepared for people to tell you things that you should be doing differently, giving you stories of how they did things and so much more. It is just a part of being pregnant, and yet another one of those things that everyone goes through while she is with child. Being prepared to hear some pretty off-the-wall statements can make dealing with them easier.

You will also want to prepare to be called "Mom" or "Mommy" by everyone. Kids love to do this, but adults are also in on it, too. This one isn't so bad, but it might come as a shock to hear it from some people, if you are not at least prepared to hear it

It is kind of nice to be called a mom, but the real treat comes when your baby says it the first time!

Stretch Marks

You have probably been waiting to see those two words this whole guide, wondering why you have yet to see any mention. But do not worry. We haven't forgotten them. We still look at them every single day so there is always that constant reminder there, even if we wanted to forget. People will tell you a lot about stretch marks. Every person has a different tale to tell: how to prevent them or how lucky she was not to get them. It is true that not all pregnant women get stretch marks, but for most women it is impossible to prevent them. If you are one of the lucky people for whom this is not an issue, you can thank your lucky stars for that. Stretch marks occur on the stomach, the arms and the legs, and oftentimes on the beasts, too. They occur due to the increase in the size, which stretches the skin, in such a short period of time. Stretch marks are often nice to see and they have a blue, red or purplish color. African American and Hispanic woman, as well as those of other dark skinned tones, are more likely to develop stretch marks and they are usually darker and deeper on these skin tones. There is not a lot that you can do about stretch marks. Watching what you eat so you do not gain a ton of extra weight is one step. Investing in a good cocoa butter lotion and using it on a regular basis can also help.

What's That Smell?

Have you ever wondered what it is like to be a drug-sniffing dog that has such a heightened sense of smell it can detect the faintest whiff of something? Well, we haven't either, but that is pretty much what it is like to be pregnant. You can smell everything and it is really intense. Many times you will find yourself asking, "What's that smell?" only to have other people tell you that they smell nothing. That is impossible, you think, because you can smell it so well. Your dog-like sense of smell is likely to develop at the very beginning of your pregnancy and continue until you have the baby. Sometimes it is a good thing and sometimes it is not, because you smell it all -- good and bad! Be prepared to have a Wonder Woman sense of smell.

The Movements Are Incredible

The first time that you feel your baby kick is an incredible feeling. It is incredible to feel all of his tiny little flutters and movements. Some people feel them earlier than others, but if you are paying close attention, you will be able to feel them quickly. Be sure that you have your journal ready to write all of these special feelings down.

Document Everything

This is probably not something that you will have any trouble doing. Most pregnant women love to take photos of their baby belly and their pregnancy, but many fail to keep a journal to document those special occasions. Do not assume that you are going to remember everything because you are not. Believe us, Mommy, you have yet to learn. There are tons of themed pregnancy journals and keepsake baby books that let you jot down those special memories and you very well should take advantage and use them. Remembering how you felt that first time you heard the sounds of that tiny heartbeat, how in love you were the moment that you found out, the first ultrasound and glimpse of your baby. These are all things that you want to document, but don't forget those other little and unexpected things. They are just as memorable and certainly a blast to look back upon later in life. Snap pictures until your snapping finger hurts, and keep everything special that happens to you documented in that special journal. You will be glad that you did this later in life.

"I Want It and I Want It NOW"

Ordinarily in life, we see something that we want and we get it when we can. Yes, some things we want more than we want other things, but nonetheless we understand and do what we can to work on getting those items. But when you are pregnant, you will have cravings that are so intense that not getting what you want at that very moment is enough to send you into a tear-filled frenzy for hours on end. The cravings of pregnant women are immense, and sometimes they are also very odd. The body craves what it is lacking in most cases, so if you are eating healthy you are less likely to have those cravings. For most women, though, there will be something that you simply cannot live without and would drive 500 miles to get it. Expect this.

Hemorrhoids

Yep, the real pain in the butt. Hemorrhoids are for old people who aren't eating their Raisin Bran. That notion is incorrect. Anyone can get a hemorrhoid at any age, and when you are pregnant the odds of its happening are even greater. It doesn't matter if you're 20 or 40; pregnancy doubles the risk of hemorrhoids. Again, it is all about the added pressure on the body, the rectal area and the weight of the uterus. Hemorrhoids really hurt, and that pain intensifies while you are pregnant. You may or may not get a hemorrhoid, but it is important to know it is possible. If you have a hemorrhoid, it is difficult to go to the bathroom and it also makes it difficult to sit, lie down or do much of anything else. There are many over-the-counter treatments for hemorrhoids, should you be one of the unlucky ones who develop them. You can also talk to your doctor about treatment options, if you are getting them on a frequent basis, if the over-the-counter products are not working or if you are simply concerned with baby's health and want the expert advice first. You can also help lower the odds of getting a hemorrhoid by eating a well-balanced diet. It isn't just the Raisin Bran that can help with a hemorrhoid; many fruits and vegetables are high in fiber content.

Four Weeks & a Wake-Up

The last month of pregnancy is definitely the hardest. While the last trimester itself is uneasy, it is those last four weeks that seem to make even the calmest, gentlest of people feel as if are going to lose their minds. Prepare to be uneasy all of the time and probably really grumpy and biting the heads off of everyone who so much as speaks to you. Emotions and mood swings are also going to be really high. Remember, all of those hormones are going crazy inside of your body! Everything is going to make you cry, and there may be people who are looking at you with a lot of wonder in their eyes. Ignore them. If they are mothers, they will understand. The last four weeks also seem like an eternity, so expect that to be something that you experience as well. Soon you will be free, but in the meantime prepare yourself and everyone around you for this last month. Once they have been warned, all is fair in pregnancy.

# Chapter 8: Your Diet And Nutrition

Diet and nutrition is key to healthy pregnancy, and often the best solution to your prenatal care. Diet is the sum of the food you eat to meet your nutritional requirements. Nutrition is how you consume and use food to nourish your body. These two go hand in hand. You need to eat a well-balanced diet to receive good nutrition your body needs for healthy pregnancy.

Healthy Diet to Meet Nutritional Needs

Nutritional needs and requirements vary depending on a number of factors such as age, gender, weight, health condition, and whether one is pregnant or not. Being pregnant, you have specific nutritional needs and requirements you should satisfy to keep your body and the life inside your body healthy. The best way to give your body good nutrition is to eat a well-balanced diet.

Earlier, you already have an idea of how much weight you should add to help you and your baby grow safe and healthy the entire span of your pregnancy. This time, you will know why eating a healthy diet is necessary to your nutrition and how it can satisfy your nutritional requirements to make sure of your safe and healthy childbirth.

Your Nutritional Needs and Requirements

While nutritional needs and requirements may vary from one pregnant woman to another, here are some standards:

You need roughly 300 added calories day-to-day. This amount can go either up or down depending on your prenatal weight together with your activity level. If you happen to carry twins in your womb, the standard increases from 300 to 500 more calories daily.

While you measure the standard in terms of quantity or the number of calories, it is crucial that you also pay attention to the quality of your caloric intake, or the kind of food that you consume. You should get your calories from healthy or nutritious food.

- Increased amount of Vitamin D. You have to know that your baby is entirely dependent on your body to meet his/her need for Vitamin D. If you are not meeting your own need for this type of vitamin, you cannot expect your baby to meet his or her own, too. Lack of this vitamin has negative effects to the physical and intellectual development of your child.
- Extra Vitamin C of about ten (10) mg daily. Your blood carries Vitamin C to different parts in your body to your baby. During this travel, you may lose a certain amount. The standard recommended allowance is 80 to 85 mg. The limit is 1800 for 18 years and below, and 2000 for 19 years and above.
- What Vitamin C does is to protect your body and your baby from infection, to strengthen bones, to repair tissues, to stimulate mental development, and to help your body absorb an essential nutrient for pregnancy that is iron.
- Folic acid or folate to prevent your unborn to contract neural defects and cleft palate. It is best to supply your body with the right amount of folate before your pregnancy and or within the first two (2) months of your term. 200 to 400 mg each day during your trimester lowers the risks for neural tube defects (birth defects that affect the mental development and spinal cord of your baby).
- Riboflavin or Vitamin B2 of 0.3 mg more each day protects your baby from heart defects, and increase in Vitamin B12 of

0.2 mg daily will help your body cope with fetus development.

The recommended amount for other nutrients stays the same for both pregnant and non-pregnant women. It is important that you meet at least the minimum standard or requirement in your nutrition. This is to give your baby the healthy environment it needs for normal growth and development until he/she is born. Depriving your body of nutrients can result to birth defects and health problems, and can even endanger both lives, yours and your baby's.

What Makes a Healthy Prenatal Diet

Your diet is the primary source to satisfy your prenatal nutrition. You have to watch your diet more carefully for the growth and development of the life you carry in your womb. Eating a healthy and well-balanced diet is a must, especially for first time moms like you.

A well-balanced prenatal diet consists of the following:

- Carbohydrates, particularly the complex type, for energy you and your baby need. The Food and Drug Administration (FDA) suggests that you should get 55% of your daily calorie need from carbohydrates.
- Choose complex carbohydrates. The body uses them longer reducing fat build-up. What you get is more energy and healthier weight gain from its consumption. They are also a good source of fiber that can help you control unnecessary food cravings.
- Protein is extremely important, as it is the nutrient that builds the foundation of good health. You should give your body about 60-70 grams of protein daily while pregnant or 15-25 gram increase from the usual daily nutrient recommendation.

The building block of cell development, protein and its amino acids are the primary nutrients responsible for fetus growth and development. Lack of it will result to several health issues and birth defects, most of which are life-endangering.

- Dietary fiber dramatically reduces the risks for health complications during your pregnancy. This is because fiber cleanses your body to flush out toxic substances. These substances are major contributors of health issues such as gestational diabetes.
- Fiber comes in two types, soluble and insoluble. Both are necessary, as each has its own specific benefits. Soluble fiber helps prevent gestational diabetes while insoluble fiber aids the digestive system and prevents constipation. Fiber will enable you to sustain healthy weight the entire course of your pregnancy.
- Vitamins and minerals are essential nutrients to keep you and your baby healthy. Remember that your baby is dependent upon you for his/her growth and development inside your womb. Essential vitamins and minerals protect the good health of your body and stimulate the best growth and development of your baby.

Certain types of food are rich in vitamins and minerals you need, such as fruits and vegetables. Natural food types are definitely better than processed food as sources of nutrients. In fact, health experts recommend natural over processed or instant food especially during pregnancy so your body receives the most nutrients you can get naturally from food.

- Water is the best way to hydrate your body, and hydration is a critical element during pregnancy. You lose more water in your body with frequent urination and perspiration while conceiving your child. You therefore need to increase your intake of water to replace what you have lost.

When your body becomes dehydrated due to lack of water, you may suffer from infection affecting the life inside you. Dehydration can also induce you to labor prematurely. To prevent unnecessary risks and complications, hydrate your body by drinking plenty of water. When it comes to drinking water, there can never be too much.

Food to Eat While Pregnant

During your pregnancy, certain food types can bring you the most benefits to improve your health and to make sure of the right nourishment for your baby. It is always best to choose food that has the most nutrients that can keep your healthy weight. Remember you need to add just the right amount of weight while you are pregnant.

The top ten foods when it comes to combined nutrients they have are the following (in no particular order):

- Asparagus is rich in fiber, folic acid, and iron, three of the most important nutrients your body should receive during pregnancy.
- Soy has vegetable protein, choline, fiber, folic acid, iron, potassium, and zinc.
- Legumes and beans are rich sources of vegetable protein, fiber, folate, iron, potassium, and zinc.
- Quinoa is a healthy seed that has lots of protein, folate, iron, and potassium.
- Milk has loads of essential vitamins and minerals like Vitamin D, B2, B12, calcium, and protein.
- Eggs are good sources of protein, choline, Vitamin B12, and selenium.

- Berries will supply your body with Vitamin C, fiber, folic acid, and they are also wealthy sources of antioxidants to protect your body from free radicals.
- Avocados are good sources of essential fats, choline, fiber, iron, potassium, and zinc.
- Salmon contains Omega 3 fatty acids, protein, Vitamin B12, and DHA or Docosahexaenoic acid, an essential fatty acid crucial to brain development.
- Yogurt has probiotic as well as Vitamin B12, calcium, and potassium.

The top ten food rich in folate or folic acid are the following (in no particular order and other than those mentioned above):

- Green leafy vegetables such as spinach. You can eat them as side dish or one of the main courses to for a well-balanced diet.
- Citrus fruits such as oranges. You can eat the fresh fruit for snack, extract the juice for refreshing beverage, or use it as an ingredient in preparing your healthy meal.
- Broccoli gives you about 24% of folate you need. It is also a savory way to detoxify your body naturally and safely during pregnancy.
- Lentils have high-density folic acid. Eating half a cup of lentils can satisfy 50% of your folate need.
- Sunflower seeds are versatile way to add folate to your diet. You can eat a handful as is as your snack, sprinkle it on your vegetable or fruit salad, and use it as an ingredient for baking. To get the most benefit, choose the unsalted variant.
- Tomatoes are also rich in folate. You can eat it raw, drink its juice, or use it as main ingredient such as with tomato soup.
- Okra is slimy but it is one vegetable loaded with folate. You can get about 37mcg of folic acid from a cup of cooked (preferably boiled or streamed) okra.

- Celery can give you 34 mcg of folate per cup. It is preferable to eat this vegetable raw or as ingredient to your fresh vegetable salad.
- Carrots are a delicious source of folic acid. It is also one of the most versatile sources to meet your daily nutrient need.

Whole grains and fortified cereals are folate boosters. Pair them with other folate sources such as broccoli, sunflower seeds, tomato juice, and others, you will experience dramatic increase in folate to satisfy your daily nutritional need.

The top ten food rich in iron (in no particular order) are the following:

Spinach is a super food that does not only contain loads of iron but other pregnancy nutrients as well. You can get about 3.2 mg of iron eating just half a cup of this super food.

Beef is a good source of iron, but choose lean beef meat for healthier way to get your nutrient. Each serving of beef meat can give you up to 3 mg of iron.

Each potato can give you 2.7 mg of iron. It is also a good source of your dietary fiber.

White beans have the highest concentration of iron among beans. It can easily give you 3.9 mg of iron per half cup.

Fortified cereals can start your day supplying your body anywhere between 2 mg to 21 mg of iron per bowl. What is best about these cereals is they are also rich in calcium and folic acid.

Prunes can satisfy both your iron and fiber needs. You can choose to eat the dried fruit or drink the juice; they both give you the same iron content.

Seaweed is rich in iron and a safe way to get Omega 3 fatty acids. It is also a good alternative to fish oils necessary for mental development of your baby.

Pumpkin seeds can really pump up your iron supply. You can eat its roasted seeds as snack, or include it as a recipe ingredient for texture and taste.

Clam chowder can give you about 23 mg of iron per bowl. Use tomato as soup base and you double the benefits, since the Vitamin C in tomato will allow your body to absorb the iron better. Tomato is also a good source of folic acid.

Liver pâté is very rich in iron. Chicken liver has high concentration of iron followed by beef liver. If you want to get the highest iron content, choose goose liver for your pâté recipe. Prepare just enough for immediate consumption as refrigerating it can expose the pâté to bacteria.

Food You Should Refrain from Eating

If certain food types help you satisfy your nutritional needs, there are those you should avoid while you are pregnant. The American Pregnancy Association lists the food as follows:

Uncooked seafood like oysters and raw meat from pork, beef, and poultry. Eating them puts you and your baby at risk for disease-causing bacteria such as salmonella. It can also cause food poisoning, which of course endangers your lives.

Fish with concentrated levels of mercury such as swordfish, shark, king mackerel among others. You can eat canned tuna but be very conservative in eating it. As much as possible avoid eating sushi or raw fish meat. To satisfy your Omega 3 fatty acid needs, you can choose to take natural dietary supplements such as fish oil. Consult your physician before taking any supplements.

Uncooked eggs to avoid the risk of salmonella. Be sure to check the ingredients as some readily available food such as mayonnaise, dressings, ice creams, or certain types of sauces and dips may use raw eggs. This is especially true for homemade recipes.

Soft types of cheese unless they only have pasteurized milk as ingredient can put you at risk for miscarriage. Similarly refrain from drinking unpasteurized milk as like soft cheese, it has Listeria, bacteria that can travel in your body to your baby and cause blood poisoning.

Caffeinated beverages can trigger miscarriages, low birth weight of your baby, and or premature childbirth. Caffeine works as a diuretic to rid of body fluids. It can result to dehydration and nutrient loss. Beverages that contain caffeine are coffee, tea, or sodas. Drink plenty of water instead. To add flavor and taste to water, you can choose to drink milk, fresh fruit or vegetable juices. You should remember though that they are not substitutes for your water necessity.

Avoid alcohol at all costs. Even the smallest amount of alcohol can already interfere with how the life inside your womb develops. It can cause serious harmful effects to your baby. Before, during, and after your pregnancy especially if you are to breastfeed your baby, you should refrain from drinking alcoholic beverages.

Unwashed fruits and vegetables. Especially with vegetables, they may contain traces of pesticides or toxic substances from the soil. It is also best to choose organic vegetables or homegrown fruits, as they are safer and has higher concentration of nutrients.

Natural Dietary Supplements

You may not meet your nutritional needs from your healthy diet alone. This is especially true for women who are not used to eating nutritious food before getting pregnant. To increase guarantee of giving the body essential nutrients, it is crucial to take dietary supplements.

However, you must exercise extreme caution and care in choosing your supplements. It is best to pick all natural food supplements that come from reliable and trustworthy manufacturers. You should also see to it to consult your physician before you take any supplements regardless of how safe they are.

Food Supplements Safe for Pregnancy

Several natural dietary supplements are available in the market. While they all claim to deliver safe results even for pregnancy, not all can bring health benefits. A few of these supplements, however, are necessary and important, some can do more harm than good, and the rests have no use at all.

Four (4) natural food supplements that are safe to take during pregnancy are the following:

Prenatal multivitamins - this is typically what physicians prescribed or recommend to their pregnant patients. It supplies the body with a combination of essential vitamins and minerals necessary for pregnancy such as iron, Vitamin B complex and D, calcium, and there are brands that have a substantial amount of folic acid as well.

Folic acid or folate - when you prenatal multivitamin does not include folate or folic acid, you can get it separately. Folic acid prevents birth defects. To maximize benefits from this nutrient, you should consume the food supplements before your pregnancy and or during the first trimester, and from then on increase the dosage up to the recommended limit.

Fiber dietary supplements are typically safe for use by pregnant women. These natural supplements help regulate hormones in the body that fluctuate during pregnancy. Fiber improves food digestion and prevents constipation. It is important that you drink a lot of water while taking dietary fiber supplements.

Fish oil food supplements are good sources of Omega 3 fatty acids. This is particularly useful to avoid harmful mercury in most fish meats. The supplements supply the body with essential fatty acids without the risks of exposure to mercury. Stay away from cod liver oil, though, as the amount of Vitamin A it has can bring adverse effects to your baby.

In choosing your food supplements, exercise extra care and caution. This is the time when being meticulous has the most benefit. See to it that you read the label and get all pertinent information about the product. Limit your choice only to those products that come from trusted brands and manufacturers. Ingredients must be all natural or organic and only the finest.

Most importantly, make sure that you consult with your physician before taking any of these food supplements. You can get recommendations from your physician and or discuss your options in taking dietary supplements to boost the meeting of or satisfaction of your nutritional needs. While food is the primary source of nutrients, supplements can fill in the gap to increase assurance that you are meeting your recommended daily intake of nutrients for your pregnancy.

What You Can Benefit from Food Supplements

The right choice of dietary supplements can bring several benefits to your pregnancy. They are the secondary sources of nutrients. Your healthy diet may not meet your specific nutritional needs. This is where supplements come in handy as they fill in the gap.

You have to keep in mind that the life inside your womb is completely dependent on your body for nourishment. When you eat, you do not just think about your own needs but also the nutritional needs of the baby you are carrying. Any nutritional deficiency on your body can take its toil on your baby.

It is also quite tedious to source all your nutrients from food. You will have to really plan hard and well and eat a lot to meet your needs. The least you would want is unnecessary stress and pressure as they are unhealthy for your baby. Dietary supplements help your body receive nutrients it needs without added calories from food.

Natural food supplements ease the burden of satisfying your nutritional needs. It does not mean, however, that you will depend your needs heavily on these supplements since they bring convenient results. As much as you can, you must source your essential nutrients from your healthy diet, as this is the best method you and your baby can benefit from your nutrition. Supplements should come in only as a gap filler. Some nutrients are difficult to source from food owing to your delicate condition.

Improve your dietary habits and start paying attention to the quality your food intake. Choose those that are highly nutritious, those that are rich in nutrients specific to healthy pregnancy but low in calories. Strive hard to meet your daily nutritional needs from food and fill in the gap by taking the right supplements. This is the best way to nourish your body so you and your baby get the most benefits.

# Chapter 9: Your Diet And Common Health Issues

Do you know that your diet plays a major role in treating and resolving common health issues during pregnancy? Often, it is the best and only solution you need to get well from health problems and ailments during your maternity period.

Natural Remedies for Morning Sickness

Morning sickness, or joint bouts of nausea and vomiting, is a popular symptom of pregnancy. Most pregnant women experience this symptom usually during the first three months. For some women, morning sickness can last the entire trimester and occurs not only in the mornings but also throughout the day.

To deal with this symptom effectively, you have to understand what triggers it. The main culprit for morning sickness is the fluctuation of your hormones, specifically the rise of your beta HCG or what you call as your pregnancy hormone.

Typically, nausea and vomiting is self-limiting. For pregnant women, this symptom goes away after the first trimester. Certain studies show that morning sickness is a mechanism of the body to protect you and your baby from the harmful effects of toxic substances.

With morning sickness comes your aversion for certain food. Amazingly, food items that you learn to hate are the types that have the most harmful chemicals. To relieve yourself of the symptom, a good natural remedy is to eat dry crackers or cereals. They are also rich in fiber and iron, two of the nutrients pregnant women need.

It also helps to limit your food intake to smaller portions but increase its frequency. You have to make sure that you are meeting your recommended nutrition with the amount and quality of food you eat. To prevent nausea and vomiting, drink your water at least half an hour before meals. You can also choose to drink it half an hour after meals. Drink plenty of water in between meals to hydrate your body.

It is best to stay away from spices and oily food. Choose to eat food that has less odor, as the smell can trigger you to feel nauseous and vomit. Ask your spouse or anyone in the family to take over the cooking chores, at least during the first trimester of your pregnancy. Give your body enough sleep.

Skin-Friendly Diet

Skin disorders and irritations are common to pregnant women, but these are the types that normally disappear after childbirth. If you want to keep your skin healthy, here is what food to eat and what food to avoid.

What Food to Eat

Here are at least five (5) food you should that serves as good nourishment for your skin. They contain nutrients to protect your skin from hormonal fluctuations to prevent or relieve skin irritations and disorders.

Avocado is rich in Vitamin E and antioxidants to protect your skin cells against damages from free radicals. This fruit has glutathione to help lighten the skin from hyper-pigmentation and keep it younger-looking.

Sweet potatoes are a power-packed source of nutrients containing Vitamins A, C, and E beneficial to the skin. You will benefit from the beta-carotene content of this food to prevent aging of the skin, specifically to delay wrinkles from showing.

Tomatoes have wealth of Vitamin C that builds collagen (protein necessary for tissue connection and support). It is also a good source of Lycopene, a substance that protects the skin from sun damage.

Walnuts keep the skin smooth and supple because of its alpha linolenic acid content. This nut is also a good source of beta-carotene and Vitamin E, and a delicious way to enjoy the healing properties of zinc.

Olive oil protects outer skin and prevents injury. It has the healthy fats the body needs and is one of the richest sources of Vitamin E, beta-carotene, and polyphenols that protect the skin from free radicals.

What Food to Avoid

If certain food brings loads of skin benefits, there are also those that are unfriendly and can worsen your skin problems. You should refrain from eating these food types.

Sweets and other food that has excess sugar are not only villains to your weight, but they can also worsen your pre-existing skin condition such as acne or fungal infection. What is more, sweets can speed up the aging of your skin to make you look older than your age.

Alcohol is a diuretic that can dehydrate your body and show on your skin. It is one food that is a completely no-no for pregnant women. It can heighten your skin problems and trigger other health issues putting you and your baby at higher health risks.

Processed and instant food contains chemical ingredients that can further disturb your already fluctuating hormones. Prevent toxic substances to enter your body and wreak havoc by avoiding this food type.

Gestational Diabetes Diet

Gestational diabetes is a health condition specific to pregnant women and easily controllable with the right diet. It is a common ailment during pregnancy where blood sugar level rises. If you fail to manage the condition, it can have serious effects on your baby.

One of the best natural ways to manage the condition is to watch your diet. Among the food groups that have dramatic influence on gestation diabetes is carbohydrates. But you cannot abstain from eating carbohydrates without disrupting your nutritional balance.

What you can do is to shift from eating food with simple carbohydrates to those that have complex carbohydrates and strictly follow a well-balanced diet. The difference between the two types of carbohydrates is their sugar content.

Simple carbohydrates have only one or two molecules of sugar that make it the fastest to digest and absorb. Unfortunately, it is also the type that has little nutritional value except rich calories. Examples of food containing simple carbohydrates are sugar, syrups, jams, jellies, soft drinks, and candies.

In contrast, complex carbohydrates have more sugar molecules that enable the body to use it longer. Since it is slow to digest, it does not mix with the blood easily. It is the type of carbohydrates that can keep your glucose or blood sugar stable. They also contain fiber that can rid your body of toxic substances and wastes efficiently. Examples are whole grains, green vegetables, beans and peas, potatoes and sweet potatoes, pumpkin, and corn.

Since your body needs energy from carbohydrates, it is best to source your energy from eating food that has complex carbohydrates. Make sure to eat just the right amount necessary to keep your diet well balanced. It also helps to supplement your diet with essential vitamins and minerals to meet your nutritional needs. Choose natural over processed food.

Strictly follow the recommended daily dietary allowance for pregnant women. Your primary source of nutrients should come from your healthy diet. Use supplements to fill nutritional gaps. Monitor your blood sugar level all throughout your pregnancy, and consult your physician regularly.

When you satisfy the nutritional needs of your body, you are activating and strengthening its own natural mechanism to protect and prevent any health issues, problems, and or diseases. Pregnancy is a delicate condition. It is wise to use natural remedies as they work with your body and not against it. However, you should always consult your physician for any remedy you wish to apply regardless if how safe it is. Getting the best of both worlds will definitely increase guarantee of safe pregnancy especially that this is your first time.

# Chapter 10: Labor And Delivery

Labor and delivery carries its own set of signs and symptoms, and things you should look out for. Unlike the three trimesters of your pregnancy, these symptoms are not going to last you very long, maybe a few hours to a few days at most. Some women may experience early labor symptoms for up to a week before labor starts, but these will generally be low in intensity until they get closer to active labor.

In this chapter, we are going to explore the signs and symptoms that labor is on the way. You will also learn about some of the basic things that you should expect in the delivery room, and how you can prepare yourself for the experience.

SIGNS OF LABOR

The following symptoms are signs that labor is preparing to start. These symptoms are generally felt at some point between 37-40 weeks, if you carry your pregnancy all the way to term. However, you may experience these symptoms earlier than that if you are going into preterm labor. If you start experiencing any of these symptoms, especially before 37 weeks, you should consult your doctor. They will tell you what to do, and when you should come in!

YOUR BABY "DROPS" INTO POSITION

Before labor starts, your baby will "drop" into position. You can tell this has happened when your baby bump is sitting lower down, and is more directed towards your pelvis. This is because the baby has officially prepared to enter the birth canal, so they are getting lined up and ready to make an appearance!

## YOUR CERVIX DILATES

Probably the most well-known symptom of labor starting is the cervix dilating. Of course, you probably can't tell this is happening, but your doctor will be able to tell you. In the days leading up to your labor, your cervix will begin to slowly dilate. Most women sit around 1-2cm for about a week or two before labor actually begins. Once labor starts, they will continue opening until they reach 10cm, which is when active labor starts.

## INCREASED CRAMPING AND LOWER BACK PAIN

You may notice more pain in your lower back and more cramping in your abdomen. This occurs as a result of your muscles preparing to put in all of the work to release your baby. This can also happen because the new position of your baby results in there being new pressures on your lower back and pelvic area. As well, your pelvis will be opening up the last little amount to let your baby come out, so your bones are quite literally stretching open.

## LOOSER JOINTS

The increased progesterone in your system are still responsible for your joints being loose, though you may notice this even more towards labor. You may experience popping or cracking in your joints a lot more, particularly when you move out of a position you've been sitting in for the same amount of time for a while.

## DIARRHEA

Many women experience diarrhea leading up to labor. This can be a displeasing opposite of the constipation that many women experience in the weeks beforehand. If you experience this, it's just because your muscles are loosening which means so are your bowel movements. Make sure you drink plenty of water, and prepare for labor to start!

## YOUR WEIGHT GAIN SLOWS DOWN, OR YOU LOSE SOME WEIGHT

Once your baby is fully "cooked" they will pretty much stop putting on weight, because they are getting ready to come out! So, if you notice you've stopped putting on pounds, or even if you lose a couple, this is why!

## YOU FEEL MORE FATIGUED THAN NORMAL

Because of your super-sized belly and all of your hormones, and the frequent need to urinate, it can be hard to get a full nights' rest. Because of this, you may find that you are consistently tired. The best thing you can do is sleep on the side closest to the washroom, and keep several pillows on hand to make those few hours of shut eye as restful as possible. As well, rest as much during the day as you can.

## YOU START NESTING

This is a common symptom of labor that you see often in the media on television shows and in movies. Nesting is a symptom many pregnant women experience towards the end of pregnancy as a means to prepare their home for the baby. If you find you suddenly have a burst of energy and all you want to do is clean and get everything ready for baby to come, it could be because baby is coming very soon!

## YOUR VAGINAL DISCHARGE CHANGES

Changes in vaginal discharge can include increased or thickened discharge, and a change in color. This is completely normal.

## YOUR CONTRACTIONS BECOME STRONGER AND MORE REGULAR

As your Braxton Hicks contractions change to actual contractions, you may notice they become a lot stronger and more regular in frequency. This is your body preparing to contract the baby out, and unless they are happening minutes apart for a long period of time, it is completely normal.

## BLOODY SHOW/MUCUS PLUG

As well as your vaginal discharge changing, you may experience your bloody show at some point. This happens as your mucus plug starts to fall out. You may notice a snot-like consistency that is streaked with blood. This is your mucus plug, and you don't need to worry about this, unless it's coming out before 37 weeks! Either way, you should tell this to your doctor just so they can be prepared for your impending labor!

## YOUR WATER BREAKS

The water breaking is one of the most famously known labor symptoms, but also happens to be one of the ones that happen the least! Only about 15% of women experience this symptom, and it's usually the last sign that labor is about to start. Make sure you let your doctor know as soon as your water breaks, especially if it breaks early.

## WHAT YOU SHOULD EXPECT IN THE DELIVERY ROOM

There are a lot of things to expect in the delivery room, and it varies based on how your pregnancy and labor have gone. If you are carrying a high-risk pregnancy, if you have a scheduled caesarean section, or if something goes wrong and your labor becomes an emergency caesarean section, you are going to have a totally different experience in the delivery room. In this chapter, we are going to only discuss what to expect in a healthy pregnancy where delivery occurs in a hospital room.

The delivery room is a scary and exciting place, and you may become overwhelmed with emotion while you are there. You are going to be going through a lot physically, and mentally. You are preparing to meet the life you've been creating for the past nine months, and that is a lot to take in! You are likely going to get hooked up to a no-stress-test machine that will make sure your fetal movements are strong and healthy, and to measure your contractions. You are also going to get your cervix checked on a fairly regular basis, to see how far you are progressing.

A good portion of your stay is going to be spent relaxing as much as possible so that you have the energy to get through the contractions. You may wish to spend some time in the shower or on a birthing ball, to help take some of the pressure and pain off of your abdomen. If it gets really hard, you may opt for pain medicines, such as laughing gas, or an epidural. If you were GBS positive, you will also be hooked up to an IV to get antibiotics every four hours.

Once labor begins, your doctor and a few nurses will come into the room. They will help coach you through pushing, and make sure your baby comes out safely. Your doctor may use forceps or a vacuum extractor to help take out your baby, if he or she needs a little assistance on the way out. Once your baby is out, your doctor will clamp the umbilical cord and let your partner cut the cord, if you have a partner involved. Then, you will be given a chance to have skin-to-skin contact with your baby, and nurse him or her. Sometime after your baby has been born, you will also have to push out your placenta, which is not a painful experience for most women, and takes minimal effort. The placenta is a tissue, so it will not stretch out your vagina as it exits your body, meaning you will likely not find it to be as painful, or painful at all.

Shortly after your baby is born, the nurses will take him or her for a few minutes to weigh your baby, and take some important measurements. You will then be able to shower off, and move into a more permanent room where you will remain for the rest of your hospital stay. About twenty-four hours after your baby is born, they will have their vitals taken to ensure that your baby is not suffering from jaundice or anything else. These are called heel-poke tests and they only take a few minutes for to do. Throughout the time you are there, your nurses will come in to check on you and your baby to ensure that you are both getting along well, and provide you with any support or assistance you may need along the way.

AN INSIGHT TO POSTPARTUM LIFE

The initial postpartum period is the hardest. You will be in "fourth trimester" until about six weeks after your baby is born. At this point, you are going to experience your postpartum bleeding, and many hormonal changes. Your body will be getting back into a balance from all of the pregnancy hormones, which can lead to many emotional and physical changes.

During these weeks, your baby is still going to have part of the umbilical cord - complete with the clamp - attached to their body. This will naturally fall off within' a few days once it dries up. Your baby may spit up a lot, which is completely normal as they are getting used to being able to digest food. Their poop is also weird, as it will be a blackish green color, or it could be yellow or brown. The color of newborn poop varies, and can also vary in texture. As long as it is not pale, you should be okay.

Getting to sleep through the night will be hard with your newborn, as they will want to eat frequently. Ideally, you should sleep during the day when your baby sleeps, at least for the first little while, as this will help you replenish the sleep you are losing through waking up all hours of the night. Having a strong support system in place is also helpful.

# Chapter 11: What to Expect - Labor Induction

Many women hear the topic of induction and they do not know exactly how to respond. The thought that your body does not want to go into labor on its own, or that your baby would be safer if they were delivered under a medical induction can be terrifying. However, if you take the time to understand the process, it will not be nearly as scary as it sounds.

What is Medical Labor Induction?

There are many medical reasons to have your labor induced. Your body naturally creates the hormones necessary to start your labor. However, some women do not create enough of the hormone to really get labor going strong enough to bring your baby into this world. Sometimes, your body just needs a little boost.

When your doctor has decided that it is time to induce your labor, he will give you an IV medication called pitocin. This will help start contractions and help to thin out your cervix.

Who Should Be Considered for Induction?

There are many reasons that your doctor may consider you for induction. These reasons are:

- gestational diabetes
- pre-eclampsia
- going past your due date (41 weeks pregnant)
- if the health of you and your baby are at risk by continuing the pregnancy
- … and other medical conditions that affect you and baby

What about inducing for non-medical reasons?

Are you just tired of being pregnant? Or does your doctor have something planned during the time of your due date? Does this have you thinking about inducing early? Did you know that almost 25 percent of the inductions are not medically necessary or are elective according to the Center for Disease Control Moms and experts are hot on the topic of induced labor during non-medical reasons.

Inducing before 39 weeks have not been recommended by the American College of Obstetricians and Gynecologists. If you induce earlier than 39 weeks there is a risk of bringing a child into the world that is not fully developed. "Induction can carry risks that should only be used for medical reasons," says Sabine Droste, MD. She is a professor at the University of Wisconsin-Madison of obstetrics and gynecology.

There are certain situations where if the doctor thinks that they are close to deliver but live too far away or won't make the drive to the hospital the doctor may make a call to induce. This would keep a birth from happening on the road, or anywhere outside of the hospital.

What are the risks of non-medical induction?

There are times when family come to see the birth of your child or we are so busy that we would like to have the delivery at a certain time. This can cause for a treat amount of temptation to induce your pregnancy because of this. Other times people think and say that you are too big and you will have to have a C-section in order to have your child. This can scare mothers to try and induce labor before truly knowing if the baby really is too big or not.

You should really think about this and be cautious because you could complicate things. Just because you induce early does not mean you will not need to have a C-section. The chances of having a C-section are about as equal of a chance as the baby actually being too big to need a C-section. You should wait to make this decision after discussing with your doctor the options you have taken and thought about.

How is labor induced?

When there is a patient that has a cervix that is insufficiently dilated, the cervix needs to be softened. We do this by using prostaglandin which is a hormone. After the cervix is softened another hormone called oxytocin is administered to help trigger labor. Pitocin is usually intravenously administered. Inducing labor is much easier when there are already signs of labor early on. This is because the body is ready to go.

There are other ways of inducing labor, such as breaking the amniotic sac releasing the amniotic fluid. This is done by puncturing the amniotic sac with a sterile plastic like hook. When the amniotic fluid is released it contains prostaglandins. This will help to increase the frequency and strength of your contractions. If this does not induce labor than there is a larger risk that infection can spread to your baby because there are no fluids to protect the baby any more.

There is a different procedure called membrane sweeping. This involves breaking the membrane connections from the uterus. This is supposed to force the cervix to start dilating and effacing which should help to start contractions.

Although these are methods that are used, it does not mean that they will always work. It all depends on how the mothers body will react when these actions are taken. The mothers body can react differently to any of these. It could cause labor to run fast and smooth or it could make things take longer.

Do natural inducers really work?

Here are popular methods that are used. You can decide for yourself if they are effective.

Walking has been used to try and help move the baby into a position that uses gravity that can help.

Stimulating your nipples can help release oxytocin and can start contractions. Although doctors give caution to this method because it can also cause contractions that will last longer and cause distress to your baby.

The Pineapple fruit has a chemical in it called bromelain. This can help to soften the tissues connected to the cervix.

Sex can be a fun way of trying to speed things along. This is because semen has cervix-softening prostaglandins in it.

Spicy foods can also help kick the body into full gear and get your innards moving. But if it does not work it could just cause you to have gas.

# Chapter 12: What to Expect – Having a C-Section

There are so many women who have their birth plan in mind through their full pregnancy.

They have memorized and read about all the details. Many end up learning that the best chance for the safety of their child is for them to be delivered through C-section. This can be upsetting when this was not the plan they had in mind all this time. This change in plans can cause the feeling of fear, guild and dread causing them to tailspin. In all reality women should always keep in mind that things can and may happen to change how the delivery of their baby may go.

The C-section is no way any woman wants the birth to go but in certain situations it becomes necessary. Here we will discuss what you can expect if your doctor says the better way is to have a C-section. Sometimes the doctor may call that a C-section should be done because of certain complications that the doctor has noticed. Other times it happens during labor when the baby is not reacting well with the contractions you are having.

When a mother hears C-section mentioned it automatically causes fear to develop. We will discuss issues that are common with unplanned C-sections.

Typical Immediate Fears

C-sections are commonly talked about and how they are so awful. This can cause instant dread and questions to flood your mind. Some of these worries are would it ruin my experience of birth? Will there be an excruciating and long recovery time? Would I be left with big ugly scars?

Will this C-section be unnecessary?

The decision in performing a C-section is made by 2 physicians. They are quite common and happen in 1 out of 4 births. Some reasons that C-sections are taken into account are for multiple pregnancy, large baby, labor failure, diabetic medical conditions, fetal distress, placenta Previa or high blood pressure.

Will the Surgery Be Long and Scary?

It is normal for any major surgery to make you apprehensive. You will feel pressure and a slight tugging when they pull the baby out. It should be a painless procedure that takes around 45 minutes. The baby is usually born within 10 to 15 minutes from the start of the operation.

Most of the C-section is performed with the mother awake. To relieve pain, the mother can have a spinal block or epidural which will numb the lower portion of the body.

Epidurals are usually used in labor and it will be topped off before the surgery of a C-section. The Spinals are given when there is a scheduled cesarean. They last only about 1 or 2 hours and can be easily administered. They reserve general anesthesia in rare cases or emergencies when the spinal or epidural does not work.

The surgery starts with an incision above the bikini line into the abdomen wall. A second incision is made in the uterus wall where the delivery of the baby takes place. They then cut the umbilical cord and remove the placenta and close the incisions.

When the surgery is all done Duramorph is usually administered for a long-lasting pain reliever. This helps for any discomfort after the spinal or epidural has stopped working.

Will this rob me of the experience of giving birth?

It is not a regular birth but the mother is awake and will experience her baby being delivered into this world and into her arms.

You should not blame yourself for a C-section and that the planned labor did not go as was planned. As long as the baby is healthy and delivered than the birth was a success. You should be happy that you just brought a life into this world.

Will a C-section prevent me from bonding with my baby?

When you have a C-section you are awake to witness it and most times you will have your baby handed to you right after birth. This allows for you to hold your baby and love them.

Will recovery be extremely painful and difficult?

You are held for around 4 days at the hospital where you will experience pain around the areas where the incisions were made. It will also be difficult to get out of bed and back in bed unassisted. You will be given a couple of types of drugs to help manage pain. Percocet will most likely be prescribed as a painkiller. Sometimes a morphine drip that can be self-administered will be given so that the patient can press a button when the pain gets to be too much.

There are ways that you can help to lower the pain and increase the speed of recovery. Drinking warm water has been suggested. This can help you to pass gas. This shows that you can start eating solid foods again. It is also suggested that if you have had a C-section that you get out of bed the day after surgery or as soon as possible.

This helps to loosen up the muscles around the incision area and can get you back to wanting to get up and go.

Medication will help to ease the pain so that you can get out of bed and you shouldn't be afraid to use it.

When you get home keep getting up and moving but don't over work yourself and do strenuous work. You will begin to feel better in as little as a week.

Will I have a scary, ugly scar?

At first the area can be red. There will be a thin scar just above your pubic hairline. The incisions are usually 5 to 6 inches in length so that there is enough room for the shoulders and head of your baby to be delivered. Over time the color and size of your scar will face where only your husband, doctor and if you have one your bikini waxer will only see. You can also look at your scar as a happy remembrance of when you brought your child into this world.

Will all of my future babies have to be born through C-section?

Doctors for the longest time always stuck with the saying that once you had a C-section you would always have a C-section. This is no longer how it is looked at. There is now a 70% success rate of vaginal birth after cesarean and it is increasing as a safe option.

But as with any surgery there can always be more complications that can cause serious risk. You should always allow your doctor to consider and evaluate if it is an option for your next birth or not. Always make sure to consult your doctor and ask those important questions in moderation during your office visits.

# Chapter 13: Preparing for Delivery

New moms have a great training tool for delivery available. Classes are a good idea for any first time mom. There are different types of classes available to any new mama that she can take advantage of. A birthing class is a great choice, you can go alone or with your partner, and you will find most hospitals offer this for first time parents. Usually this is free of charge. That is helpful because as you know you are starting to spend a lot of money on the new baby! A birthing class will walk you through delivery step by step.

Truth time. You are probably going to see a movie showing someone actually giving birth. It may make you swoon in anticipation of your big day or it may make you want to vomit. If the latter feeling overtakes you do not worry. This is normal. When it is your body and your baby it suddenly will not seem icky in any way. If you take a class at the hospital you plan to deliver at that is great because they will take you on a tour of the hospital and birthing area. Now if you find out that you will be in a room with another mom during delivery do not despair. When you are in labor you will just plain not care. All you will be focused on is working through the contractions, controlling the pain, and preparing to meet your new bundle of joy. Of course, there will be a curtain separating the two laboring mothers so you will have privacy.

Birthing classes will also teach you the importance of how to breathe. You may have seen a movie where a mom gives birth. It may seem funny when the mom is "hee hee hoo hooing" however that type of breathing is most beneficial and really does help to control the pain!

After the baby is born you will either breastfeed or bottle-feed. The choice is yours. However, you do need to be aware that breastfeeding is extremely good for your child. Especially, the first few days when the colostrum is in your breasts before your milk lets down. There may be reasons you are unsure about breastfeeding. Do you have to go back to work? You can work and breastfeed. You can pump on your lunch and breastfeed before and after work and throughout the night. You can also choose to alternate bottle and breast. Breastfeed when you are home and let the baby drink formula when you are working. That is ok! Some breast milk will still give your baby all the necessary and helpful nutrients that she needs. There will be classes after the baby is born on breastfeeding. If you are having difficulty or not sure about breastfeeding then these classes would be helpful to you. Also, most if not all hospitals have lactation consultants and they will help you. Not to mention, they will definitely understand all the feelings you are having and work you through it.

Have you thought about the birth experience yet? There are several things you need to decide. Who do you want in the room with you when you are giving birth? Yes, you may want visitors during labor and that is different than giving birth. When you are ready to push the stirrups come out and privacy disappears. The choice of who to have in the room with you when you are bringing a child into this world is a very personal decision. You may only want your partner. You may want your partner and your mom. You might not care who is in there. The hospital usually only lets two people in the room at a time though. If you originally thought that you wanted perhaps your mom or his mom in the room and you change your mind that is ok. It is hard to let someone know that you no longer want anyone in the room. This is one of the times that you will be so happy to have your nurse around. Labor and delivery nurses have no bones about telling visitors that they cannot come in the room. In fact, they will probably lie for you and say it is their decision to avoid any hurt feelings. Remember though, this is your big day! Just like a wedding you get to make the decisions. If someone's feelings get hurt that is okay, they will get over it. When you are laboring to bring your child into this world it is up to you, and only you, who is there with you.

It is a good idea to have some sort of birth plan. First up, drugs. Do you plan on getting an epidural? Do you plan on delivering natural? You should have a general idea of what you want and do not be shy about speaking up. Truth time. You may change your mind. That is ok! If you planned on going completely natural and the pain is getting too intense for you then it is okay to get the epidural. Do not feel bad about this. You are not a wimp. You are a smart woman who is doing what is best for her and her child. On the other hand, you may be doing okay and decide to hold off on the epidural and end up going natural. If you are trying to go natural and at the last minute decide you want an epidural it may be too late. There is a point where it is about to be pushing time that the doctor will no longer allow the epidural to be administered.

Another thing to decide is do you want to walk around or lie down throughout the contractions. Again, you may very well change your mind. If the contractions start to slow down walking the halls of the maternity ward can help to speed it back up. Do you want music? Do you want to use an exercise ball to roll on? No matter what you decide make sure it is about making you as comfortable as possible during the labor and delivery experience.

# Chapter 14: What to Expect - Bringing Baby Home

No matter how many children you have, bringing every new baby home is a unique experience. No two babies are the same, which surprises many parents. This is especially the case when they bring home a new baby and their personality is the exact opposite of their previous children. The truth is, every child is different, and many of these differences are noticeable as soon as their baby comes into this world.

Ten Important Facts About Newborns

Let's face it, you never know exactly what to expect from a newborn, especially if you are a new parent. Here are ten important facts that you should know about newborns that no one else will tell you.

1.      Your baby may look, well, strange. Baby's heads typically appear squished for a few weeks. This is because they were repeatedly squished as they passed through the birth canal. Also, newborn's faces are typically puffy and a little swollen. Some babies may have bruises on the bonier places of their face too.

2.      Your baby won't reward you for at least the first six weeks. Every parent looks forward to hearing their new baby coo and smile. Unfortunately, baby's typically do not reach these milestones until they are about six weeks old. Don't worry, it is well worth the wait.

3.      Babies must have a sponge bath until their umbilical cord falls off. This usually takes about two weeks. The good news is that babies do not really get dirty at this age, so getting a few sponge baths will not cause hygiene problems.

4.      Your baby's soft spot is not as sensitive as you would think. It is just fine to brush his hair and touch his head. You may feel the soft spot pulsate when you touch it, but this is only because of the blood vessels surrounding the area.

5.      Your baby WILL let you know if she is getting enough food. Your baby should eat every two to three hours at first. However, if she is hungry more often, she will definitely let you know. Many pediatricians are slowly moving toward mothers feeding their baby's at will, rather than keeping them on a strict schedule. Over time, your baby will regulate her eating habits to a set schedule.

6.      Babies have dry skin and their isn't much you can do about it. Think about it like this. If you spent 9 months floating around in a pool and decided to get out, your skin would dry out over a few days too. While you do not technically have to do anything about it, you can apply some Johnson's pink baby lotion if it makes you feel better.

7.      You and baby are not hostages when you come home. You can come and go whenever you and baby please. The only thing you must ensure is that anyone who touches your baby must wash their hands first.

8.      Babies cry ALOT. This is how your baby communicates. These ear piercing screams will let you know that your baby is hungry, cold, has a messy diaper, or wants you to hold them. The only problem is that these early conversations can be extremely frustrating for both of you. Over time, you will learn what each wail means.

9.      Babies may sleep a lot, but they do not sleep for long stretches of time. It is important that you wake your baby up every three hours to get changed and eat. Do not wake your baby up during the night, they will wake up if they need something. By following

this schedule, your baby will learn the difference between day and night schedules.

10. The first few weeks will be the most stressed, lonely and tired days of your life. These are the difficult times that prepare you for the rest of parenting. Rest assured, it will get better faster than you think.

Leaving the Hospital

Do not overdress your newborn baby for his or her 1st trip home. If you think you will be too warm in a knitted cap during the day, think that the same will apply to your baby. It is alright to dress your baby in a baby blanket over bare legs or a T-shirt and light cotton pants when the weather is warm. During cooler or cold days, you can wrap your baby in a hat, footsie pajamas and warm blanket. But always check that the blanket is far from the face of your face to prevent him or her from being suffocated. It is also important that you choose clothes simple clothes that do not need a lot of pulling and pushing of your newborn baby's legs and arms. Before you leave the hospital, make sure that you have raised all your questions to your doctor so that you will have peace of mind when you get home.

During the Car Trip

The car seat is considered as the most essential thing you need during your baby's first trip home. All states require parents to ensure that their babies have a car seat before they leave the hospital. You can opt to buy, rent or borrow a car seat even before your due date. This will give you enough time to carefully inspect the car seat for safety. You can choose between infant-only car seats or convertible car seats. If you decide on an infant-only car seat, make sure that you replace it when your baby grows to more than 22 to 35 lbs. Many parents prefer a convertible car seat so that they will not need to buy a new one when their baby grows older.

First-Time Emotions

It is natural to have mixed emotions during your baby's first trip home. This is particularly true for first-time parents. There will be both nervousness and excitement. You may also feel sore and physically drained, depending on your experiences during labor and delivery. Your mixed emotions can also be the result of hormone imbalances caused by the childbirth.

You may also start to feel anxious as you think about the needs of not only of your newborn baby but the needs of your partner and other kids, as well. Even visits from family and friends can add to your stress level. Amidst all these emotions, it is very important that you talk to and seek help from your partner and other loved ones who are willing to help.

When to Call the Doctor

Pediatricians are used to first-time moms calling them often during the first few weeks after the baby is born. First-time moms, in particular, can worry too much even for the littlest things. If ever you come to a point when you are not sure whether to call your doctor or not, here are some signs that can tell to do so immediately:

1.   More than 8 diarrhea stools within eight hours.

2.      Rectal temperature is 38 degrees Celsius (100.4 degrees Fahrenheit) or higher. This is particularly important for babies younger than two months.

3.   Bloody stool or vomit

4.   Symptoms of dehydration such as no wet diapers in six to eight hours, a depression in the soft spot on the head of the baby and sunken eyes.

5.   Inability to keep fluids down or repeated forceful vomiting.

6.   A soft spot that protrudes when your baby is upright and quiet.

7.   Labored or rapid breathing. Immediately call 911 when you notice that your baby starts to turn bluish around the mouth or lips and has difficulty in breathing.

8.   When your baby is difficult to rouse.


Always be aware of your new baby's condition. Even minor conditions can at times change rapidly for young babies.

# Chapter 15: Tips for First Time Moms

1. Prepare Your Mind

Your Whole Life Will Change

So let me put it to you straight. Whether you planned your pregnancy or it "just happened", being a Mom will change your life. Your entire life. I'm sure you've heard this before, just as you're hearing it from me now. You probably won't totally understand it until you're holding your child in your arms and have taken care of him or her for the first few weeks. Still, I'll try to explain. Your life without children is free and your responsibilities are based on what you need and what needs to be done to maintain your life and needs. When you bring a child into your life, you still need to take care of yourself, yes. But your main priority is making sure your child has everything he or she needs and is safe. For example, in your life without a child, if you have some extra money or want to do something special for yourself you may go get your nails or hair done. With a child, there may not be extra money. Or if there is, you'll probably spend it on your little one instead of yourself. A mom usually does (and should) think about what her child needs before herself. You will start thinking this way when your child is born, but you should start rearranging the way you think now so it will be an easier transition.

Think About Who You Allow In Your Life

Not only should you start to think differently about financial priorities, but about who you allow in your life, and now your child's life. Childless, you have only yourself to think about when choosing what relationships you allow in your life. When I say relationships, I mean romantic and otherwise. If you're single and pregnant, now is not the time to start a new romantic relationship. Now is the time to focus on being ready for your child. If you're already in a relationship with the baby's father (your boyfriend or husband), make sure that you have open communication with him about how you're going to parent your child together. Also, fix any problems you have in your relationship because your relationship problems will affect your child's life. If you have any friends or family who you know aren't good for you or are negative about the baby, keep them at a distance or let them know that you don't want any negativity in your life and around your child. Any close unhealthy relationships in your life can affect your child by causing him or her stress and can even delay development.

Don't Stress

Bringing a child into the world is going to change your life, yes, but don't stress yourself out! There will be less time for yourself. There is a whole other life to consider, yes. But you still need to take care of yourself. In order to be a good mom, you do need to make sure you're healthy too. Whatever stress you're dealing with will affect your child too. Being organized with your time will help to decrease stress. Taking time for yourself will also be important. Even a five minute break can center you and refocus your mind. You may find yourself hiding in the bathroom at some point in time to get a breather! Some good ways to destress are taking a walk (with or without your baby), sitting down and drinking a cup of hot tea, or reading a book for five or ten minutes.

2. Take Care Of Your Body

Take Care Of Yourself

Pregnancy takes your body through a lot. If you're planning to get pregnant, start getting your body in the best shape possible now. If you're already pregnant, you'll be limited in what exercises you can do, but still take care of yourself and do what you can do. Definitely ask your doctor what's safe. You want your body to be strong and prepared for the birth.

Exercise

Like I said, if you're already pregnant, there will be limited exercises you can do. Especially if you're a beginner exerciser. Moving your body and being fit will still be important. If you can do nothing else, walking is always a good option. Swimming is low impact and is good for pregnant women. It can be done at any stage of pregnancy. There are other options, but again, make sure you ask your doctor what's safe for you. Especially if you have health risks. After giving birth, the time to wait to begin exercise again is usually six weeks. You'll want to start doing safe exercises as soon as possible to get your body back into shape so that you can keep up with that little one! You may not have as much energy after delivery, and getting into an exercise routine will help your body get its strength back, as well as lose any extra baby weight. Of course, what you're putting into your body is important too...

Diet

Exercising to stay in shape is important, but it goes hand in hand with your diet. When you're a new mom, what you eat is more important. The importance of eating for energy becomes more evident. If you eat too much junk food, you will notice! Recovering from the pregnancy and delivery and at the same time, adjusting to having a new baby can take a toll on your body. You need to continue taking vitamins. Make sure that you make time to eat enough. And make what you do eat count! Include vegetables and leafy greens in your diet like broccoli, kale, spinach, and carrots. When you go shopping, check out the produce section and try new vegetables you haven't tried or didn't like before. Also, eat protein sources like chicken breast, eggs, Greek yogurt and beans. Calcium is one of the most important minerals for women to pay attention to, so drink milk and eat yogurt or cheese. If you don't eat dairy, try alternative calcium sources like soy milk, or take a calcium supplement. Finally, after grocery shopping, don't be afraid to try something new in the kitchen! When your little one grows into a toddler, you're going to need to try new dishes for his or her little taste buds anyway!

Pampering Yourself

As a mom, no one is going to take care of you more than you can take care of yourself. No, pampering yourself is not frivolous, either! It's important for your mental well being, as well as your physical well being. After all of that washing and sanitizing, put lotion on your hands. Wear a pretty scent you enjoy. Buy yourself a new nail polish. Light a candle and enjoy a few minutes of a book or drink some tea or coffee. Or wear some nice lacy underwear under your mom clothes. These are just a few examples of pampering yourself, but you can come up with some of your own, based off of what you enjoy.

3. Change Your Priorities

Getting Into A Routine

You're not number one anymore! This can take some getting used to. At the newborn stage of your child's life, you may feel like you don't even have time to take a shower some days. All of the appointments you need to keep, being up late hours of the night feeding, washing dirty baby clothes, preparing bottles, etc. Taking care of a newborn takes up most of your time. Getting into a routine will help you to stay sane as well as stay on track with everything that needs to be done. If you're lucky enough to have someone to help you the first few weeks, good for you. Not everyone does, but that can definitely be an advantage. As you're learning your baby, try to set the same time of day for washing and filling bottles, laundry, nap time and bed time.

## Your New Obligations

Being that you have more to do on a daily basis, you may need to learn to say no and cut some things out of your life. Before you welcome your child into the world, it's easier to fit fun activities such as date nights and time with friends into your schedule, but with a child, especially a newborn, it's not so convenient. You'll be staying home with your child a lot. Finding a babysitter isn't always so easy. For the first few weeks, you should keep your baby home in order not to expose him or her to extra germs and sick people anyway. Also, there will probably be a lot of people who want to visit and see the new addition to your family. Let some of them know that you don't want visitors for the time being. You're just getting your family adjusted to having a new little one and don't need extra company to entertain.

## Remember To Stay Positive

So you're giving your baby the majority of your time, and your body is healing at the same time. It's easy to be stressed with everything going on. Keep it in your mind that your baby is a blessing and a positive addition to your life! Being a mother is not an easy job, but it's rewarding and helps you see what's most important in life.

## 4. Get Ready To Change Your Schedule

### Get A Planner Or Calendar

To be successful and to make the most out of your time as a mom, you need to have a good schedule. I strongly suggest having a planner or calendar where you plan what you're doing with your time and for taking notes. To make it fun, pick one that's cute and fits your personality. Even go and get hilighters to mark the most important points. If you choose a calendar, hang it in a place where you'll always see it. Write down every doctor appointment, mark down feeding times, family events you need to remember, even grocery lists and lists of household chores that need to be done. Your planner will be like a reference to keep track of your time.

Planning Ahead

Your schedule will be different if you're working than if you're a stay at home mom, but is important either way. Have a plan for your days from start to finish. Plan what time you'll get up. Make sure it's before you know your child will wake up so that you'll have time to shower, get dressed and get your focus. You'll have time to pray or meditate if that's a part of your life, and write look over your schedule to see what you have planned for the day. Also, it will be so much easier for you to shower and get dressed by yourself than when your little one is already awake and demanding your attention. Getting up earlier may be forfeiting a little sleep, but your day will go so much better.

Your Diaper Bag

A really important part of preparing for your days will be your diaper bag. Leaving the house with your baby unprepared can be very inconvenient. Keeping the diaper bag ready with everything in it, kept in the same spot can make things go smoother when you're getting ready to take baby out. Some essentials you'll need to keep in there will be diapers, baby wipes, an extra change of clothes, prepared bottles, a toy to keep your little one busy, snacks for an older baby or toddler, and a cloth to wipe any spit up.

5. Buying Baby Items

Where Your Baby Will Sleep

One of your biggest purchases you'll make for your baby is going to be a crib. There are different options you have for where your baby will sleep. A lot of cribs nowadays are designed for the stages of life. The crib stage, when your baby is first born and through the first year. It will convert into a toddler bed when your baby is ready, then into a big kid bed. There's also the option of buying a bassinet for your newborn. It takes up less space, but can only be used for a few months, until your little one is too big for it. Something that you'll need, whether your baby sleeps in it or not, is a pack and play. A pack and play is a portable play pen that you can put your baby in during the day to play in and stay safe while you're busy and watching close by. This can also be where he or she sleeps. You can choose this option if you're trying to conserve space or for travel. It can be folded up when not in use and taken with you if you're spending the night somewhere besides home with baby. The choice is yours, just make sure that baby is safe wherever he or she is sleeping. It is not a good idea to have your baby sleep in bed with you.

Diapers And Wipes

This will be your biggest expense! It's a good idea to stock up. If you're planning on having a baby shower, you'll probably get a lot if there are a good number of people coming. If you want to, instead of a baby shower, you can throw a diaper party. Just cook some food and invite friends and family over, asking them to bring diapers for the baby. It's not important to buy all one brand. What is important is that when you stock up or have people buy them, that different sizes are purchased. When baby comes, pay attention to how he or she reacts to the diapers. If your little one gets a rash from one brand of diapers, don't buy those ones anymore! Same goes for baby wipes. Your best bet is getting unscented baby wipes.

Bottles

Unless you're exclusively breast feeding and you're not storing milk (it's all coming straight from you to your baby), you're going to need to buy bottles. There are so many different brands and types of bottles, so I suggest that you go shopping and look around. See what your options are. The most important thing will be the nipple on the bottle and whether your baby is taking the milk from it. The same with a pacifier. If you buy different pacifiers, you'll soon know which one is your little one's favorite.

Clothes

When buying clothes for your baby, keep in mind how quickly your baby will grow. So you may not want to go out and buy the most expensive clothes you can find for your baby. I know you'll want to get some cute things for your little one. That's natural. So why not buy a special outfit for each holiday? If you have family members who have older kids and have left over baby clothes they won't use again, they may want to hand them down to you.

Car Seat And Stroller

With both a car seat and stroller, you have so many to choose from. Again, I suggest that you look at your options. Go online and research what's out there. Even go in the stores and see what they have. Choose which is right for you. Keep in mind that most hospitals will want to check that your car seat is safe before letting you take the baby home with it. You may want to ask to make sure.

Other Items

There are so many extra baby items out there on the market that you won't necessarily need but may want to consider A couple of them include baby bottle sanitizers and baby wipe warmers. Part of the fun of preparing for baby is shopping!

6. Your Support System

A good support system will be a big help to you when you have your baby.  Knowing who to call and who to trust when you need someone to watch your child is valuable. It will help you to stay sane as a busy mother, and will be a benefit to your child. Your support system doesn't have to be huge either. If you get overwhelmed and need some rest or need to go somewhere important where you can't take your child with you, have at least one or two people you can call.

 When you think of all of the people you know, you can come up with all of the people you know that you'd trust to watch your child. Whether it's your mom or dad, sister or brother, best friend, or your neighbor who you've known for years. Before the baby is even here, go to each one of the people you trust and want to be a part of your support system. Let them know that you would like them to be a part of your child's life. Ask them if they'd be available to watch your child at times. Find out what their schedules are. After the conversation you have with each person you want to be a part of your support system, if they are good fit to be a baby sitter, write their name, phone number and address in your planner.

Knowing who you're going to call when you need someone to watch your little one, and even who you're going to call when you need some new mother advice is another way to be prepared going into motherhood. If you go through your mental Rolodex and can't think of anyone you would trust with your child, find people! For support as a mother, there are so many different forums and support groups to be a part of where women come together and have created their own community. Google "mom support group forums online" and there are many places online that you'll find to be a solace to you. Another option you have if you'd rather meet people face to face is to join a group for mothers in your community. Ask your local hospital, church, or community center about groups there are for mothers in your area. A big plus is that usually, there will be childcare at a support group for mothers.

## 7. Welcoming Your Little One

### The Hospital

After all of the preparation you've done changing your priorities, getting mentally and physically ready for baby and buying baby items, now comes the time to welcome your new baby into your home. First, lets talk about the hospital. Make sure that you bring the car seat to the hospital when you go in to deliver. Also, make sure that you pack a bag for yourself and the baby. Include a change of clothes for yourself and a robe. Put socks, clean underwear and a pair of slippers in your bag. Remember a camera for pictures. You'll want to capture those first moments of life. For the baby, pack an outfit for him or her to go home in. Also, bring a baby blanket. You won't need to bring diapers because the hospital with will supply you with them during your stay.

### Your House

Before you go into labor, set up your baby's bedroom. Put the crib together. Set up the dresser and put away any clothes you have for him or her. If you have a changing table, set that up too. Also, clean the house so that it's freshly sanitized. That way, you won't be frantically cleaning when you bring your new baby home and he or she won't get sick from any left over germs. Another good idea is having meals prepared for the first couple of weeks. Even freeze some things that you can thaw so that the food will last for two or three weeks. That is, if you don't have anyone to help you by bringing over anything. It will just make the transition welcoming your little one into your home that much easier.

### Utilizing Your Support System

Let certain people on your list of people to call know when you go into the hospital to deliver. That way, they can plan to come and help you when you bring your baby home. Like I said earlier on, don't invite everybody over the first few weeks. You don't want too many people in your house when you're adjusting to having your baby home. Just one or two people who will be helping out. Helping you prepare meals or clean. Maybe watching the baby while you get some rest to recover from delivery.

Enjoy Your Baby!

After preparing for your baby and welcoming him or her into your home, you're adjusting to a new way of life. Don't forget to enjoy every stage! Time goes by and your little one will grow so quickly. Enjoy the spitting up, changing diapers and late nights up putting him or her back to sleep just as much as the cuteness. Soon, he or she will be in the toddler stage and you'll be dealing with potty training. Enjoy it all! You only get one chance at them being small. So make the most of it!

# Conclusion

Having a new baby is an exciting and stressful time for many. From all of the symptoms you will experience physically to all of the emotions you will experience that will mentally weigh on you, there is a lot you will go through. It is important that you brace yourself for everything that is to come.

Having this audio guidebook is a great way to recognize what symptoms are normal, and which are alarming. You can also prepare yourself for each trimester, and ensure that you are taking the best possible care of yourself. Even though pregnancy is a largely physical experience, you should also do your best to slow down and enjoy it. This may not be easy, especially if you are experiencing difficult symptoms or a high-risk pregnancy, but it is important since this experience is one you only get to have once in a lifetime.

It is important that you prepare yourself for childbirth well in advance, and that you maintain open lines of communication with everyone involved. The more open you are and honest you are about how you are feeling, the easier this process will be for you.

Most importantly, stay calm and relaxed as much as possible, and nurture yourself in every way that you can to make this process as easy and as comfortable for you and your baby as possible.

Thank you.

CPSIA information can be obtained
at www.ICGtesting.com
Printed in the USA
LVHW080103150720
660698LV00018B/393